SLIDE

James Buchan was for ten years a foreign correspondent of the *Financial Times*. He has published two previous novels: *A Parish of Rich Women* (which won the David Higham Prize, the *Yorkshire Post* First Novel Award and the Whitbread Prize for Best First Novel, and was runner-up for the Betty Trask Award) and *Davy Chadwick*.

JAMES BUCHAN

Slide

Minerva

A Minerva Paperback
SLIDE

First published in Great Britain 1991
by William Heinemann Ltd
This Minerva edition published 1992
by Mandarin Paperbacks
Michelin House, 81 Fulham Road, London SW3 6RB

Minerva is an imprint of the Octopus Publishing Group,
a division of Reed International Books Limited

Copyright © James Buchan 1991

Chapter One first appeared in the Summer 1989
issue of *Grand Street*. Chapter Five appeared,
in different form, in *20 Under 35* (Sceptre, 1988)

A CIP catalogue record for this title
is available from the British Library
ISBN 0 7493 9911 2

Printed and bound in Great Britain
by Cox & Wyman Ltd, Reading, Berks

Again, when in my youth, attending my father on a journey to the Catskill Mountains, in the government of New-York; having nearly ascended the peak of Gilead, being youthful and vigorous in the pursuit of botanical and novel objects, I had gained the summit of a steep and rocky precipice, a-head of our guide; when just entering a shady vale, I saw, at the root of a small shrub, a singular and beautiful appearance, which I remember to have instantly apprehended to be a large kind of Fungus which we call Jews ears, and was just drawing back my foot to kick it over; when at the instant, my father being near, cried out, 'A rattle snake, my son!'

William Bartram

ONE

Gardner

Wherever I've lived in the last fifteen years, I've always had with me a set of old china plates, chipped and scuffed under the glaze. I bought them in a village outside Isfahan: I think it was called Faisalabad, which is a common place-name in Iran. I know I walked there one Friday, because that was the day I did not teach. I'm not sure about much else, because I went to many villages during the time I lived in Iran. The plates have probably gathered loose recollections of the country and that time in my life, as a magnet arranges iron filings in a pattern.

That Friday, I walked along the edge of the river from the old Safavid bridge in the middle of Isfahan. The river was more a marsh than a stream. The shore was muddy and scattered with Pepsi cans, cold picnic-fires, plastic bottles, twists of newspaper, fruit-skins and shit. I hated the garbage, which seemed all wrong in such a famous and beautiful city. The main road above the river was cleaner but drivers kept stopping to offer me a lift. I liked to walk.

A path ran off between small fields and I took it. I'm not sure if this was spring or autumn. If it was spring, a pomegranate tree was probably in flower. If it was autumn, there were yellow plane-tree leaves on the path. The sky was blue, but it always is blue in Isfahan, spring or autumn.

I came to two low mud walls and an old man in white slippers and cap, walking between them. I greeted him but he ignored me. Growing out of the walls were thorn-bushes. A little further on, a small boy was sitting on the ground, picking a scab on his shin. Children ran out of a house behind him and took up stations on the wall. Another boy with a glazed eye asked me home to meet his father. I said I had business and became gruff and then embarrassed at my gruffness.

In the middle of the village was a cramped open space, with three old walnut trees for shade, a well and a green tin shrine fluttering with rags. A man wearing a European jacket took my arm and shooed off the children. He led me into a house, which turned out to be a junk shop.

I went to junk shops all over Iran. I thought perhaps I'd deal in Islamic handicrafts when I'd finished Oxford. I needed to improve my eye. What I usually saw was this: cast-iron chandeliers, Chinese porcelain of the type called *famille rose*, papier-mâché pen-cases, red Bohemian glass, carpets, scraps of chintz and brocade. I drank sweet tea from saucers till my teeth ached or ate a lunch of stew or rice and minced meat, brought in covered tin dishes from the dealer's home. Afterwards, I lounged against a bolster or knelt before a brass brazier, smoking opium out of a pipe with a transfer of a nineteenth-century shah on the bowl. I was used to Persian hospitality.

4

What I remember from the shop in Faisalabad was a shelf which partly covered the only window. On the shelf were stacks of plates and dishes. Most of them looked ordinary to me. I met Iranians in villages who talked of porcelain as if it were made by magic and they put a high value on any old piece of china. For all I know, they still do.

Blue and gold caught my eye and I got all the china down. Dispersed among it was part of a European dinner service: eight plates, four with flat bases, four with raised rims for soup. All were scratched under their glazes. The only decoration was on the rims, where dark-blue lozenges were enclosed in flaking gold leaf.

I turned one of the plates over. Stamped in the middle of the base was a man on horseback killing a dragon with his lance. Beneath the knight were these words:

I can't read Russian script unless I know what I'm looking for. I knew Saint George was the hallmark of Francis Gardner, an Englishman who went to Moscow to set up a porcelain factory for Catherine the Great some time in the middle of the eighteenth century. Later on, the factory made teapots and cups for the towns of Central Asia. I remember one pot in a Kabul tea-shop that was so much repaired it was more metal than china.

5

When I tried to buy it, the tea-boy, then the whole shop, laughed and laughed.

This time, I saw the signature and decided I would buy the plates, even if they cost all the money I had from teaching, which was £50. I must have decided at that moment that I wouldn't need the money, that I could go back to England with something to show from Iran that my sister and friends could understand and admire.

I allowed myself to think of England. I could hang the plates on a wall or have people eat off them, while I wondered out loud how they'd got from Moscow to Isfahan. They might (I'd say) have come with the household of the Russian envoy, or with a carpet-dealer, a Cossack officer training the Shah's army, a Baku oilman, a railroad or telegraph contractor, a spy. I know I felt I was completing a circle, taking the plates back to the country of their maker.

I tried to be offhand, but failed. The men in the shop shook their heads and sucked their teeth. One man said the plates were from Paris. The others picked up the name and repeated it till their ideas of glamour and romance got tangled in mine and I wanted to shout in frustration. In the end, I paid £20 in English money.

I may have taken the plates away then or I came back for them the next Friday. They were packed in straw in an oblong cardboard box and then tied with a rope twined from rags of many different colours. I know I took them away in a taxi, the box wedged between my feet and the driver's seat.

I rented a room in Isfahan from an old Jewish lady called Mrs Mohandes. She disapproved of me because

I was a long way from my family, drank beer and wine and spent my time with carpet- and antique-dealers, who she said were all notorious smokers of opium. Her coldness distressed me because I was not used to making a bad impression unless I wanted to.

She was sitting in her small garden when I pulled up in the taxi but she showed no interest in either the taxi or my parcel. I offered to show her all the same. I started unpacking the plates under her best tree, which was a quince.

As I set out the plates, I saw something was wrong. One of them had a blue rim, but it was so crudely painted I don't know how I could have thought it was part of the service. Mrs Mohandes spotted it at once. 'I have the same,' she said. She pointed at the odd plate. 'It comes from the Petroleum Company when you buy kerosene.'

I have forgotten almost all the Persian I knew then but I remember the words for 'petroleum' and 'company' because I heard them often from my room in the days afterwards. Mrs Mohandes told my story to the old man who looked after her trees, to the postman and to her daughter when she visited. I was so saddened by the waste of money that I left the unmatched plate on the top of the wardrobe in my room when I left.

I did worse with my friends.

I spent much of my time when I was not teaching with two brothers, Ali and Amir Abbas Najafi, who worked in their father's carpet shop in the wide street that runs down to the Safavid bridge. The street was then called Pahlavi Avenue and their shop Pahlavi

Carpets, after the Shah's family name, and both must have different names since the Revolution.

I used to call at the shop on my way to the school and on my way back. If I did not come, they asked me what I had done instead. I thought at first that they liked me in the shop because my presence reassured foreign tourists. I am not sure now. The brothers spoke every European language between them and each summer took carpets over to a shop in Munich and another in Barcelona. It is possible they liked me. Ali, who was proud of his spoken Persian, had me recite well-known passages from literature and corrected my pronunciation. I sat for hours on a pile of carpets or walked barefoot down the soft canyons, feeling insecure, luxurious and bored.

I hadn't wanted to tell them about the Gardner plates. But their curiosity was fluid like water. It advanced until it met resistance, then surrounded the object in its path. They asked about my Friday, my walk, the village, the shop, the dealer. I wanted their good opinion. Ali drove me to Mrs Mohandes's to pick up the plates. He unpacked them expertly back at the shop.

Nobody said anything for a while. Then the brothers, who often forgot that I could understand them when they spoke Persian, burst into chatter. Their words were scathing and hurt. Their father picked up a plate and flicked it with his little finger. It rang hollow.

'Pottery,' he said, and laughed close up to me. He had uneven yellow teeth. 'It's not even porcelain, just pottery,' he said. The brothers laughed.

The old man flicked the plate again. 'You were

robbed,' he said. 'You would not be robbed by your friends.'

Mr Mahluji, a building contractor who liked to wear a cashmere coat draped on his shoulders, asked me how much the plates cost. He was the old man's partner and I told him. He told the boys to give me a rug for that price, rose, wrapped his coat round his shoulders and left.

I didn't care. I was leaving. The plates were Gardner. What did Iranians know of Gardner or England or Russia or even porcelain except the Cantonese junk they prized so highly? In the evenings at Mrs Mohandes's, I used to take the plates down from the wardrobe so I could read the maker's mark again. Even Mr Mahluji's present I accepted with bad grace. I waited a week then looked through the whole stock while Ali pushed and pulled and folded carpets and grumbled. The brothers sent it to England at their expense.

A stamp in my old passport says that I left Iran and entered Turkey at Bazargan on 10 March, 1976. I travelled by bus. There was snow on Mount Ararat to the right of the road. An Afghan man had the seat beside me. Once he unwound his turban and filled the bus with orange silk. I carried the plates on my lap.

In Istanbul, I bought a bus ticket to Cologne. It was all I could afford. I thought that I could hitch-hike to Ostend on the Belgian coast. I kept my last £10 to cover the ferry ride to Dover.

The new bus was full of Turkish men who were travelling to jobs in West Germany. Blonde women sat with them. Beside me was a Bulgarian boy, who had a sack of fruit and shared it, because I had no money for food. I dozed much of the way. In Austria, I woke once and was amazed by the green of the fields. The bus broke down in Stuttgart.

I spent £5 of my £10 on a train ticket to Cologne. I spent the night stretched out on a platform bench, the box with the plates under my head. Trains came in and went out all night and I was cold for the first time in a year. At midnight, two young policemen woke me to see my passport but they let me keep my bench.

In the morning, I spent £1 on a loaf of bread and a bus to the highway. A truck took me to Brussels. There I walked in the rain through a cobbled suburb where lighted pubs smelt of French fried potatoes and beer. The plates felt heavy and I put them down at each traffic light. I had no watch, so I do not know how long it took me to reach the other side of town. It was certainly dark by the time I got to the ramp to the highway.

A West German businessman picked me up in a Mercedes-Benz. He took me to Bruges. The lights on the highway made my eyes ache. I told him I was a student, because I'd heard Germans were sentimental about students. I hoped he would stop for food. He didn't but he went out of his way to leave me on the Ostend road. It was raining hard but a Belgian man stopped and took me all the way to the ferry terminal. When I asked him his profession, he said: *Je m'occupe avec le vide*. He was a vacuum engineer. His phrase haunted me for days afterwards.

I remember the last ferry was at 10 p.m. The fare was £8 or £9. I had £5. I had known in Stuttgart that I wouldn't have enough but I'd put the thought from my mind. I went into the men's room and combed my hair. I selected families with women. I tried to speak well. An English diplomat finally made up the difference, muttering pleasantly about the young. I told him about the plates and the breakdown in Stuttgart. Once on the boat, I avoided him.

In Dover, I sat in the immigration shed, freezing among familiar accents, until 9.30 in the morning when the bank opened. The bank notes felt large and elaborate. I took trains to London and then Tisborough. On the second train, I saw my sister and we embraced, giggling, in front of the commuters.

That evening, we sat up late round the kitchen table and I told stories of Iran. I found myself simplifying what happened, sometimes changing the point halfway through a story. In two days or three days, I felt restless and went to Oxford, though the university was still closed.

I took the plates for identification at the Ashmolean Museum. I unpacked them on a conference table in an upstairs room. A young man came in softly, looked at the plates without touching them and looked at me. I showed him the factory mark and told him all I knew about Gardner. He went out, returned with a book and opened it at a picture of an opulent service Gardner made for Catherine the Great. On the facing page was a set of factory marks for identification. My Saint George and dragon looked most like the mark used between 1804 and 1812. I asked the young man if the plates were damaged because they did not ring. He tapped one and then said the Ashmolean did not give valuations. I should try one of the auction houses, he said. I never did.

The next year, I left university and the Tisborough house was sold. I packed the plates myself. During the move, a soup plate broke in half. There was talk of pinning the pieces and my brother-in-law said he knew a man in Barnes who did first-class repairs. But I lost the pieces, I don't know how.

I had no luck in the antiques trade. I was apprenticed to a Persian from Hamadan who had a shop on Marylebone High Street. He had no use for me after six months. I started on my own and put what little money I had into a small and very threadbare seventeenth-century carpet which I bought at auction in Ipswich. I did not know that the carpet was known all over the trade and was unsaleable. Then the Revolution happened in Iran and the price of everything fell and I gave up.

I went into the foreign service and then quit that, too. In Bonn, I had a Turkish maid who broke one of the plates in the dishwasher. Another broke while my things were being shipped to New York. I have four plates left, which I keep in a cupboard.

I am thirty-five. I have owned these plates for fifteen of their one hundred and eighty years. What I want to know is this. If I had not bought the plates, would there now be eight of them or four of them or more or fewer? If I had left the plates in Faisalabad, would I know there were such a place, with three old walnut trees, near Isfahan? Is there?

TWO

Coincidence

Julie was fifteen when we started going out in 1975. I was at Oxford. We met in London, at a party I hadn't been asked to. The people who brought me dispersed. I walked through the downstairs rooms and into the garden, and then came back in and sat down on a sofa with some whisky. I was stoned from the van ride up.

I don't know how Julie came to be sitting on my right, but we were talking and she sat up, turned, and kissed me on the lips. We went into the paved garden, and I tried to take her dress off, but she bent forward at the knees and kept the dress pressed down with one arm, while she rested the other on the back of my neck. I thought: this is what I've been waiting for, a girl resting her arm on my neck, standing on tip-toe, kissing me.

We walked through the house and into the street, which was in Chelsea somewhere. I stopped Julie at each street corner, to kiss her. She had a blue suede jacket, which she left on a post-box when we stopped, and I ran back for it. She let me in through a basement door to a cluttered room with a bunk bed. She took all her clothes off, except a pair of red-and-white striped knickers, which she wouldn't take off because she said she wasn't on the pill.

She woke me up early. She was wearing a green school uniform with the tie undone at the top. In a café on the King's Road, I drank a Coca-Cola because I'd heard it was as good as brushing your teeth, and then rode for hours through hot stations to Hanger Lane, where there was a place to stop cars going down on to the M40.

How could I have broken up with Julie? I know she embarrassed me: her name, her age, even her creamy blonde hair because it went to the shoulder and split at the ends, the half-crown gap in her front teeth, the way she sat so badly and never changed her clothes or wore a bra or had any money, the way she'd slept with so many guys.

I used to meet her off the train on Friday evening. She was the last to get down. Dons and commuters pushed past me; the train pulled out; I'd turn to go, and she'd be there, right at the end of the platform, not wearing shoes or carrying just the Ferragamo handbag her mother had given her or with one hand inky from an exploded pen. In my rooms, she never said anything when people were there, just sat on the floor, making joints the size of tampons.

Christopher Stone said: 'She may well be dynamite in bed. I do not understand such things. But when it comes to conversation –' he stopped, pointed the middle fingers of both hands stiffly at the floor, laughed sharply, shut his eyes, then said, 'When it comes to conversation, you can forget Julie!' I said something about her being young, but Christopher wagged his

16

finger. He affected what I'd now call an extreme hedonism: age and sex were contingent quantities in the pursuit of pleasure. He used to say that, for himself, he was not a paederast, but he saw no objection in principle to the practice.

Christopher Stone was in his fifties when I knew him. He was keeper of Indian painting at the Victoria & Albert Museum in London. I met him the same summer, also at a party, this time at the Professor of Arabic's house up the Woodstock Road. I came into the garden and saw, under a white rose gone helplessly wild, a man with long grey hair, talking and laughing much louder than anybody else and waving his glass about. I found myself circling the shaggy lawn, getting closer and closer, always aware of his position in relation to me. It was late by the time I was talking to him. The roses seemed to burn in the gloom. Christopher said he must have dinner: had a drink, now have dinner. He paid for me and some other people at an Indian restaurant in Summertown, where the waiters made a fuss of him. He slept on the floor of my sitting-room.

I was amazed that he slept on my floor. I was amazed at how much money he had and how much he knew. He said he hated Islamic literature; it hadn't occurred to me that you could like or dislike the texts I had to read: it was a matter of understanding them. He used to read Arabic or Persian an inch from his face, because he didn't wear glasses for his short sight. I now see he must have been vain once, like me.

Christopher owned three terraced houses on the Kentish Town Road in north London, just past a railway viaduct. Built on the front were shops: a newsagent, a Cypriot café and one empty and boarded with plywood sheet. Beneath the unlet shop was a basement room where Christopher did all his living, or so it seemed because I never saw another room. He sat cross-legged just inside the door, with a tray on the floor beside him and on it a bottle of something and a Persian lacquer pen-case, and then the room receded past mounds of books and clothes to indeterminate walls. I always meant to look upstairs, maybe find myself a room and clean it up, but I always woke up in the basement, sometimes with my arm round Christopher. At break-fast, Christopher's Anglo-Indian voice boomed in the small café. Armoured with my hangover, I didn't mind.

I never asked Christopher about his life. He was brought up in Calcutta. His father had been in business. The Kentish Town houses came, I think, from his mother's side. As I went up there more, I saw a young man with short hair and a black leather jacket, who was called Steven. He had an antiques stall in Camden Lock. Once they dressed up and went down to a pub in Earl's Court which had a reputation for being heavy. For a while, Christopher went round with his arm in a filthy plaster, which may have had something to do with that.

In Oxford, I thought sometimes I heard Christopher's voice at the back of shops or his loud, sharp laugh across a crowded bar. I wore his Harvie & Hudson shirts. I gestured with my middle fingers pointed stiffly at the ground. I said to Julie: 'For God's sake, woman, have a drink!' Julie stuck out her tongue. She wouldn't let me call her darling.

I kept them apart. I went with Julie to her parents'

cottage in Surrey. Her mother was beautiful and astonishingly ignorant. Her stepfather owned a business that made steel forms for the building industry. He set me small tests: to guess where a wine came from or smoke a Havana cigar without losing the ash. I suppose he was flirting with Julie, though I didn't recognize that then. I hated being around him. I tried asking him about business and his racing boat and I tried drinking enough to pass out. The only quarrels I had with Julie were in this house.

Oxford went down. We hitch-hiked to a dance in Devon and then to Wales somewhere to stay with people we'd met at the dance. Julie mixed grass with amphetamine sulphate and shared it with hippies when they picked us up. Julie had no patience. She liked making love in fields: I remember green wheat, and chalk dirt on my lips and under my finger-nails, and the roar of the Cirencester roundabout the other side of a dry-stone wall. The sulphate kept us awake for nights in different mattress beds. The first birds singing overwhelmed me with sadness.

Julie came to Tisborough. We walked from the motorway. Elderflowers hung over the lane from steep verges. We slept in my mother's old room, because it had a double bed. Julie had a fake pearl necklace which broke while we were making love. I picked the pearls out from under her back, her shoulder blades, her side, her bottom. (Much later, after Iran, I found a sling-back shoe without a heel and a packet of contraceptive pills under the bow-fronted chest.) My brother-in-law asked did Julie's mother know she was here.

Julie went to Surrey and Christopher came, on a

motorbike, his arms wrapped tightly about Steven's waist. Steven was dealing and had a plastic bag of trips. We sat by the Nene and watched cabin-cruisers move slowly by. Christopher's long grey hair seemed like a nest of snakes. We drank whisky all night to come down. At eight, my sister came in, grey with sleep, in a red nightgown trimmed with lace. I didn't go home again till after Iran.

I thought I was going off my head. Print vanished and reappeared on the page. The evening sky tipped up over Bramerton Street and I grabbed the railings, while Julie gaped from the basement door. My mouth tasted of stale water. I said to Christopher I wouldn't get a degree unless I went. He accused me of self-denial. 'Don't think for a moment that I will give you anything,' he said but he did: £100 in £10 notes. Julie burst into tears and her tears seemed to be coming out of every part of her. Then she lifted her right knee on to my hip as if she were climbing a tree, which I always loved. Anyway, she had to go to the Dordogne with her parents.

At the beginning of August, we went back to Oxford. It was the works holiday at British Leyland. For two weeks, I scraped and then washed the ceiling of the assembly plant. The industrial cleaner I used soaked through my gloves and made me shout with pain from the steel rafters: the shout echoed round and round the empty shop. We lived in a sunny squat off the Iffley Road and I saved £190. When it was time for Julie to go to France, I walked her to the end of the road, kissed her, and then watched her bare feet all the way to the Plain.

I used some of the money for an air ticket to Istanbul. In a café called the Pudding Shop in Sultanahmet, I sat down at a table with a German boy in a Moroccan waistcoat. He was driving a second-hand Mercedes from Munich to Tabriz. I joined the convoy, taking the driving with him in turns. Tabriz was brilliant with electric light. I went to Qazvin, where I drank a bottle of vodka with a traffic policeman and slept under a quilt with his sons. I got a job in Tehran, teaching English to Air Force cadets. I lived on the roof of a downtown hotel, where steel bedsteads were arranged in three straight rows. On weekend evenings, I smoked heroin and watched the sun dissolve in dirt and smoke or went drinking in the bars along Lalehzar. Once the hotel guard wouldn't let me back in and I walked downhill for hours on an avenue that was warm and dusty and quiet. I came on some iron gates, which two young soldiers opened on to a garden criss-crossed with irrigation channels. I walked in and thought one of the soldiers came with me, but when I turned he wasn't there. As I lay down, I thought I'd fallen out of the world; and, falling, left behind the smog, the heroin and drink, the cadets with their shaved heads, the heat, the smell of petrol, the language which wouldn't say what I wanted. I woke up in the garden of the Golestan Palace. A bit later, I sent this poem to Christopher in imitation of the drunken Chinese poets he admired:

> Our cousin moon
> Rattles in mulberry branches
> Swims in far-away canals.
> Too late!
> Sleep scatters us with leaves.

We stagger up.
The sun is high.
Delegations hurry by.

I got nothing back, but then I never had a letter from Christopher.

I quarrelled with the Air Force about money. An officer threw an onyx ashtray at my head, but it missed and hit an Indian male secretary. I left Tehran and went to Isfahan. At a private school called the Language House, a teacher who had been four years in San Diego, California, sat down beside me in the staff room and said: 'I think young guys should do what they want. But these people are kind of slow. It's a generation thing.' I cut my hair. I took calligraphy lessons and made myself a wooden pen. I spent a lot of time in junk shops: in one, during Ramazan, I heard for the first time Khomeini's sermons on cassette. I wrote to Julie twice and got one letter back, saying she'd left home, to a place in Willesden. My work permit expired and I went travelling for a month, and then for two more months. In Kabul, on a bitterly cold day when the slush had got into my boots, I bought a bag of unpolished lapis lazuli of poor quality. I thought a jeweller in London could make them up into a necklace for Julie.

I went back to England in the spring of 1976. I went straight to Oxford, because I wanted to work, but Oxford Persian wasn't Isfahan Persian: the books I wanted had long gone from the library and the Iranian graduate students were in a hurry, didn't want to talk politics. At the door of the Oriental Institute, a girl said she'd heard Christopher Stone had left the V & A, and raised her dark eyebrows.

I rang Bramerton Street for days. When I didn't expect it, Julie's stepfather answered. He said Julie was in Surrey. She'd been ill and I'd better get my arse down there. He said I could take the Yamaha. I thought I'd get to the cottage and ride the bike across the lawn and right into the low room where Julie would be lying. It was a beautiful hot day and the piston seized in the cylinder on the Hog's Back by Guildford. I coasted down to Guildford station, took the bike back by train to Waterloo, wheeled it over the river, and started again the next morning by thumb. I had to walk for an hour past cottage gardens and small fields with horse jumps in them. At the house, Julie's mother was sitting in a deck chair, wearing a sarong. She waved but didn't get up. Julie was inside, stretched out on a flower-print sofa, with a pair of headsets on, her eyes closed. She'd cut her hair. She kissed me quickly and I felt bones in her chest.

She said: 'No drink. No gear. No making love. Dr Marsh says so.'

She talked about people I didn't know, new bands I hadn't heard of. Her cheeks had red in them and her eyes gleamed like the backs of big fish I'd seen early in the morning in the Karachi market. At one point, I threw the headsets at the wall. Julie got up and retrieved them.

Her mother went out to dinner, stooping to miss the beams as she put in her earrings. Julie said: 'You blokes only want what you can't have.' She let her left foot fall to the carpet. While we made love, she looked away. I looked at the chintz.

'I've brought you something from Afghanistan.'

Julie didn't turn. 'No smoke. Dr Marsh says.'

I said: 'It's being set in London. I'll send it.'

'Why? I've got to come up for Marsh.'

I rode up to London early in a hot, slow train. I couldn't read for impatience. I called the museum from a telephone box at the station, but the department said Christopher was at Bond Street and gave me another number.

He answered at the second or third ring. He said: 'I most certainly was not sacked. I merely felt the atavistic pull of trade. A snob such as you would not understand.'

'Is Steven with you?'

'Not at this precise moment,' he said. 'But in a corporate sense, as it were, he is.'

I bought a bottle of Teacher's whisky at an off-licence with a wire grille over the window. I waited at a bus stop by the roundabout in front of the station, but I was too restless, and I started walking and then was over the river and still no bus had come. I looked at every girl I passed. I thought I would burst with longing. My shins ached from the jarring pavement.

Christopher's gallery was up a steep flight of stairs, above a women's clothes shop, opposite Fenwick's department store. He let me in with a buzzer. There was a single room, not large, and a kitchen. Two windows were open over Bond Street. The place smelled of paint and the rope matting on the floor. Nothing was being shown except a Luristan bronze of a male dancer

24

on a plinth, very beautiful, and a framed page of Kufic calligraphy propped up against the skirting-board, also beautiful. For the first time, I envied Steven.

Between the windows, Christopher had made his usual nest. There was half a Turkoman saddle-bag spread on the floor and a bottle of red wine and a glass with a scummy rim. He kissed me on both cheeks, took the whisky and put it quickly in the kitchen. I squatted down in front of the saddle-bag.

We spoke together.

'Where's Steven?'

'How's that shitty Shah?'

I remembered something I'd seen or heard about astronauts: that when they came back from space, they were fractionally older or younger than those who stayed behind on earth. A bit later, after Christopher had got up and brought the whisky from the kitchen, I said this to him and he nodded sagely. I said:

'Why the fuck did you sell Kentish Town?'

Christopher leaned back against the window sill and closed his eyes. He said: 'I did not sell Kentish Town, as you put it. I sold one house and one store. The distinction is not unimportant.'

'Does Steven get a salary?'

He opened one eye. 'Steven receives maintenance.'

Through the open window, I saw the pale stucco walls of Fenwick's. The sound of traffic came in, and the smell of hot cement and petrol. Two young men were talking on the pavement. I felt light-headed and articulate. I knew I could start a sentence, without knowing where it was going, then see an end and get the sentence there, triumphantly, on an exhausted breath. I said:

'Julie Waters has hepatitis.'

'A or B?'

'The junkie one.'

Christopher laughed. 'My dear Richard,' he said, and then went back to laughing. He swayed backwards and forwards on his rug. 'My dear Richard,' he said, gesturing with his two middle fingers, 'my dear Richard, even you must have grasped by now: in the pursuit of pleasure, some must fall by the wayside.'

I burst into tears. I walked to the stairs, but then thought it would be a good idea to pick up the bronze and throw it through the window. It felt surprisingly warm in my hand. Christopher flinched and put his arm over his face, then dropped it. He looked – if this is possible – both scared and eager.

He said: 'Put that bloody fake down. Have a drink, for pity's sake.'

We finished the bottle. For some time, we spoke Persian: Christopher's accent was old-fashioned but accurate. Fenwick's green electric sign came on. He got up with difficulty from his rug. 'Dinner,' he said.

'Can't. Must go. Sober up. My sister's.'

'Fuck your sister. Be consistent, can't you, for once in your life? You've had a drink, you have dinner.'

I put my arm round his neck. 'You all right?'

'Of course I'm all right, as you put it. I generally go to The Standard at around this time. Kemal looks after me.'

'Don't pick up any trade.'

26

Christopher squinted at me. 'Why on earth would I do that?'

I missed the top step, bumped twice on the stairs, lunged for and caught the door handle, which swung slowly outwards, dropping me neatly on my knees on the pavement. Above me was a dress shop, with a polished wooden floor and just three dresses hanging on a rail at the back. I walked uphill for a bit and reached Oxford Street, which I recognized.

I was meeting Julie at the doctor's in Devonshire Place, at half-past nine in the morning. My hangover frightened me. I lay in bed till I was late, then ran out for a taxi. I had a bruise on my hip. The sun was bright and yesterday's shirt stuck to the small of my back.

In Devonshire Place, Julie and her mother were sitting in the back of a double-parked Mercedes. A chauffeur with a cap got out and stood by his door. Julie's mother lowered her window, and moved her face a little for a kiss.

When we got to the corner, Julie said: 'Off to sunny France. Out of temptation's way.'

Oxford Street was a river of people. I looked at Julie's clothes, up and down, up and down, so I would remember them but I can't. She was looking straight ahead, where Bond Street wound away downhill into heat and traffic.

We came to Fenwick's. My jeweller was opposite. I showed Julie to the door, stiffly, with courtesy, but I paused myself in the sunshine so I could remember the moment.

I looked up the street and down the street. Beside the jeweller was a women's clothes shop, with three black dresses hanging from a rack at the back. I looked up at Christopher's and Steven's gallery. Both windows were open. In the left-hand window, hanging over the sill, was a hank of hair, long and grey and matted with blood. Round Christopher's head was a bandage wound tight as a helmet.

Through the jeweller's door, I could see Julie looking at me, her eyes gleaming.

Forgive me, both of you.

THREE

Dancing

My first foreign posting was in Kuwait, where I went in 1979 as Press and Information Secretary at the Embassy. Brian Barchard was Ambassador. It was a good job, or was a good job until the Kurt Axel thing blew up. *Stern* magazine in West Germany even accused me of covering up evidence. People in London knew better, or should have done, but I know I was tainted with the affair, like poor Brian. It's one reason I left the Office.

I don't know what happened that night at the Hinkleys, except what everybody else knows. Kurt Axel was found by Caroline Hinkley on the bed in the spare room of their apartment on Water Tower Road at about noon on 11 June, 1980. He was wearing underpants. Caroline went up about an hour later, with some tea, and he was lying in the same position, on his back, with his left arm across his mouth. She told Brian that she didn't remember Kurt Axel staying, but then she didn't remember anything much about the party.

The first autopsy was done at the Kuwait General Hospital, but only on 15 June. The cause of death was found to have been alcohol poisoning. Bill Hinkley told

Brian he'd bought some siddiqi for the party, just in case his man couldn't get whisky. Two further autopsies were done for Axel's brother Dieter in Bremen after the Kuwaiti Justice Ministry released the body in early 1981. They found bruises to the head and ears that were 'congruent with' (entsprach) a heavy blow or fall.

The British and West German press made a lot of the Bremen autopsies, but I always thought the body had been so messed about by then that it was useless as evidence. Anyway, the Kuwaitis had already expelled the Hinkleys and seemed to want nothing to do with the case. Because they wanted alcohol poisoning, London wanted alcohol and so did Brian.

I don't think I met Kurt Axel, but I heard of him while he was alive and I may have seen him a couple of times. Brian Barchard had a habit of saying: 'Do you know Mr – ?' or 'Have you come across Sheikh – bin – ?' when he was intrigued by a new person. I came back from Christmas in England, and it was Herr Axel this and Herr Axel that. He worked for Dolfbau, a Hamburg engineering firm which was project manager on the second phase of the new university. His Arabic was supposed to be good. He played the viola, and Brian was always trying to organize chamber concerts.

What brought Kurt Axel in with the Hinkleys, who were certainly not musical, was horses. I found out later that he kept a horse at the stables at Kilo Ten, which is where the Hinkleys used to ride. They were mad about horses.

If I did see Kurt Axel, it was at Brian's and Reema's quite soon after I got back from London, standing side-on to me, wearing a white linen suit, talking to three or four people. He had straw-like hair tied in a pony-tail. Over the crash of the air-conditioner, I could just hear him say: 'Below five thousand metres, it is not so interesting.' Brian, who did nothing more energetic than go to the same Bach festival in Austria each August, loved this sort of thing.

I saw this person again on Thursday, at the money-changers in the suq, talking loudly in Lebanese Arabic. He had his right foot up on the banker's money-chest. His right hand was in front of him, fingers and thumb pressed together and pointed upwards in the Arab gesture for Patience! or Listen! I thought – God knows why – that he was gay.

I certainly did know the Hinkleys, but only after they came out of jail. I met them their first day free, in the basketball court of the International School, where somebody was putting on *HMS Pinafore*. It was typical of Brian that he brought them. There was a party after-wards, which was dry. The cast moved through the crowd, in bustles or striped tee-shirts, giddy with excitement, make-up striped with sweat. Bill Hinkley was on his own, in a damp short-sleeve shirt and a tie, holding a plastic cup. For somebody so burly, he seemed shy.

'How was prison?'

He looked down into his cup, which dripped conden-sation onto the polished boards. I thought I'd been too flippant. Then he said: 'Not bad, really. For me. It's quite nice, really, if you've got a bit of the scratch.' He looked up, and he was smiling. 'Poor Caro was in with the Somali tarts.' He had an Irish accent: Belfast, it turned out. I liked him from the beginning.

The Hinkleys were still under house arrest; or rather, Brian had guaranteed they wouldn't do a bunk. We moved them into an empty bungalow in the compound. It was a week or so before I realized that caution had got the better of Brian's love of celebrity. At the end of morning meeting, he'd say, in my general direction: 'And what news of Mrs Hinkley?' I saw that I was supposed to be doing the looking after.

At the weekends, which were Thursday and Friday in Kuwait, I got a bottle of vodka from the American commissary and took the Hinkleys camping in the desert or on the Gulf shore. Bill once did a strip-tease, in the flare of a butane lamp, down to some paisley-pattern Y-fronts, with everybody clapping and shouting him on. The sun had freckled him to oatmeal.

Often I went with them to the stables at Kilo Ten, which were run by a ferocious old American called McSwain. There was a hyrax in a cage and a peregrine falcon which died when the Omani groom fed it a piece of frozen American steak. The place smelled of dust and dung. Bill once schooled a sheikh's horse all one blazing afternoon, round and round on the end of a long rein, while I sat in the shade of some casuarina trees and Caroline called out to him from the rails.

Caroline Hinkley was from Yorkshire. Her father had been Sir Godfrey Crozier, a truly catastrophic governor of Aden in the 1960s. We had his memoirs in the Embassy library. Caroline had some money, because Bill once told me that he'd saved nothing from his contract: fucking Cosgrove, useless company, should've fucking stayed in UK. 'Rather his social superior, it appears,' Brian said once, and then giggled.

She was half a head taller than Bill or me, and very thin, though you could only tell this at the beach or in her riding clothes because she wore big dresses to the ground like other foreign women. She often used the third person instead of the first: 'Will Verey get Caroline another little drink?' If she wanted a light for her cigarette, she pointed to the end of it. Once, when we were camping on the beach, she sunbathed topless. I stared at a sea like boiling mercury, rather than look at her small bosoms. That evening, or maybe the Friday evening, we sat round the Embassy pool very late. I didn't know what I was waiting up for, until I saw Bill's head teeter to the side, mouth open, his left arm dangle, his cigarette fizz on the wet concrete. Caroline's chair squeaked, then I knew.

A week or two later – 4 September, 1980, I have the newspaper cutting – the *Bild* in Germany said that the British Foreign Office was suppressing evidence of foul play. There was a picture of Kurt Axel in his pony-tail, very blurred; of Dieter Axel, behind a desk with a view of Bremen harbour through a window; and of Bill in a morning-coat – at his wedding to Caroline, I suppose. On 6 September, Brian was called to the Interior Ministry and then he drove the Hinkleys to the airport. He told me to tell people the shari'a court had found them guilty of two offences: possessing alcohol and staging a gathering at which the sexes danced promiscuously together. They'd been sentenced to time served and stripped of their Kuwaiti pension rights.

I know something else, but it happened much later, and I'm not sure it amounts to anything. I didn't see the Hinkleys for nearly ten years. I left the Foreign

Office, went into the City, was sent to New York, married, had a daughter. I saw them again at Cheltenham Races, a month after getting back from America. I had some money, for the first time in my life, and I was thinking maybe I should get a horse or part of a horse. Anne stayed in London, to look after Katherine, because we had no help.

This was 1988, the year that the mare Sweet Nothing won the Gold Cup for the first time. It rained all week, and they sent out helicopters to dry the going with their blades. There was no commentary on the far side. The horses burst out of the gloom at the third last. I moved in a slow crowd from the paddock to the stands and back to the paddock again.

Beyond the finish were two rows of big white tents. Banners whipped on aluminium poles above them, advertising corporations. Through open tent flaps came the sound of television and laughter. The lane between the rows was deep in mud. Men in tight grey-green coats and trilbies hurried by. A woman picked her way down in the wrong shoes. In front of the Costain tent, I saw a big man bent slightly to the side, as if drunk or thinking hard. I walked on a bit till I remembered his name, then came back.

'Hello, Bill Hinkley.'

'Hi.' He had grey in his wiry black hair and was heavier, which made me wonder how much worse I looked. 'Have a drink,' he said, and pointed vaguely at the Cosgrove tent-door. Then he recognized me, because he said: 'Owe you enough.'

'Nice mare,' I said. I'd heard somebody say that.

'And I buy Minstrel fucking Song! At the same fucking sale!'

'Terrible going.' Clipped speech seemed right for the place.

'Terrible beast,' he said.

He led the way into the tent. The security man's eyes flickered across me to a pink badge hanging from Bill's lapel.

I said: 'So what's the Trainer's badge?'

'Not me. Caro. At Clonmel.' He turned round and smiled, which reminded me how much I'd liked him: 'A good long way from the gentlemen of the press.'

The tent smelled of wet clothes and cigar smoke. Electric fires laid down bands of heat, which were separated by bands of cold. Caroline was sitting at a round table, in a black-and-white checked suit and a hat with a small veil, with people sitting and standing round.

She said: 'If it isn't Mr Blowjob himself.'

'I'm sorry about Minstrel Song.'

'He's yours,' she said. Other people laughed. She said: 'We assume you're coming to Gay's.'

'You must be joking.'

We sat round the table till after the last race. A man from the company kept putting champagne bottles on the table. The place was hypnotic with Irish speech. I looked up once and Caroline was gone: to put Minstrel Song in his box, I suppose. A bit later, I got up to ring Anne, but then I thought I'd sound too drunk and we'd fight. I took Bill in my car, which took a long time to find in the dark field. He peed on the wheel of a Bentley.

We drove to a stone house, the other side of the

M4. Bill knew the way. The house had a stable block. Caroline was already there, sitting on the fender before a log fire, her hands between her knees. On the walls were paintings of animals, heavily cleaned. The host was a man, very shy.

He said: 'Where do you think Wall Street's going?'

I took a breath, and saw Caroline in the doorway, beckoning with a wide, slow swing of her arm. She sat in the front of the car, smoking and fumbling with the cassette-player. Bill had a glass of whisky with him in the back. We came to another big house, also with stables, and with cars parked at crazy angles in front of a portico. In the lighted front was a man in a dinner-jacket, his hair swept back off his forehead.

'Fucking cunt,' he shouted, opening his arms.

'Cunt yourself,' said Caroline, running up the steps.

'And fucking Bill-cunt! And who the fuck is this? Get out, cunt.'

'Richard Verey. Gay Moulson. Richard Verey. New owner.'

'Potential owner,' I said.

'Potential cunt,' said Gay, turning sideways to let me past.

The room was already crowded with people. There were more horse pictures under lights, and, on an oak table against the back of a sofa, a bronze of a horse that reached almost to the ceiling. Around its bronze legs were figures of people: a jockey with a whip, a man in coat and trilby, a woman carrying binoculars, but so out of scale to the horse that they didn't reach his hocks. They looked like donors in an Italian altarpiece.

Caroline and Gay were standing each side of a blazing

fireplace. He was talking about her and another man in a jacuzzi bath. She was telling a story about him getting into the wrong bedroom somewhere in Ireland. They laughed; they approached or stood back from each other; they prodded each other in the chest; they shouted. Sometimes they shouted each other into silence and conversation started to pick up in other parts of the room, till Gay bellowed:

'Floozy in the jacuzzi! Floozy in the jacuzzi!'

'So funny, Gay,' said a woman beside me.

'Great girl, Caro,' I said.

'Great girl.'

Bill was sitting deep in the sofa, which had pale-blue candy-stripes. I sat down beside him.

'Fucks the stable lads,' he said, his voice rising to a shout at the end.

'Got to go, old boy,' I said. 'London.'

Bill stared ahead of him and then got up and went to the drinks table to fill his glass.

I said goodbye to Gay. 'Fuck off then,' he said, putting his arm round my shoulder. Then he said: 'Buy, sell or hold?'

'Verey's not going, is he?'

'I must, Caroline.'

'Wee wifey waiting?'

'And wee baby-ey.'

She reached out and took both my hands. She held them for a moment, then fell slowly backwards. Long nails bit into the base of my fingers. She began to swing to her right.

'Dance,' she said quietly. 'Dance. Everybody dance.'

Her legs were stiff together. I pulled her up, but she

swung round to my left, brushed a chess table covered in things, upset the fire irons in a clatter. I had to lean back and swing her over the fender.

'Dance,' Gay shouted. 'Dance, cunts.'

She was falling. Her hair swept a Persian rug. Her eyes were wide open, looking past me or at nothing at all. I felt my balance go. I hit the chess table, and felt it sway and teeter over. The bronze horse danced. Picture lights. Mouths agape. Blue stripes. A burst of sparks. Black shoes. Kurt Axel.

FOUR

Felicia Hrabek

When people talked about Poland – and my friends talked a lot about Poland in the 1980s because of the Solidarity thing – I used to say I'd heard Popieluszko preach midnight mass at St. Stanislaw's church in Warsaw on Christmas Eve of 1983. This was while I was still a diplomat.

People used to nod or look intelligent, though they needn't have bothered: the story doesn't have much point. Jerzy Popieluszko was abducted by three police-men, locked up in the trunk of a car, taken to a wood, beaten with a truncheon wrapped in cloth, hanged and then thrown in a reservoir. His killers were tried in public, and the trial seemed to demoralize the military government, though nobody said the whole system of government would soon come tumbling down, not even Walesa or people who were supposed to know Poland well, like Klaus Arnim. I used to say all this, and then tell my story. I came to an end. My friends still wore their clever looks. Embarrassed, I'd get up to clear the plates or get more wine. Slowly, conversation picked up again.

What I never said is that I went with Felicia Hrabek,

or that I wouldn't have been in Warsaw at all but for Felicia Hrabek. I find it hard to think about Felicia Hrabek, let alone talk about her. I can just about manage her in Germany: in the Schubertallee in Bonn, say, stepping up the crazy paving of my garden in high heels, a belt pulled tight to show her beautiful waist, late, furious about something; or slumped over the rattling telex machine in the Pressehaus, her head in her hands; or walking quickly across the bridge over the Oder, the train vibrating against my back and the Polish conductor running after her, his satchel bobbing, and beyond them two men fishing through the ice.

Let me try Poland. Felicia Hrabek is four steps above me on the outside stairs of a tall apartment block in Warsaw. The walls are brown with rain. The wet air smells of coal. Felicia halts, seems uncertain. Just as I come up, she pushes against a swing door, puts her shoulder to it, and it opens.

There is no light inside, no carpet or lino underfoot, just cold concrete and something that scratches against the nails in my shoe soles. I wait, listening to rain, indistinct voices, indistinct music. Then a lighted door appears, some way away, and standing in it, a small woman drying her hands on an apron. The room is full of people, all standing up, and queuing to embrace Felicia. It is warm and smells of drink and sugar. In the corner is a colour television set – Felicia said they always bought colour television sets – on at full blast.

In my right hand, I have a linzertorte; in my left, a bottle of kirsch and a plastic bag containing two spinning-reels that cost 110 Deutsche Mark each from Schrotts in Bonn. Felicia's grandmother takes these things off

44

me, and then pushes me down on a chair beside Felicia, at a table with small plates of sausage and bony carp and black bread. Felicia's two uncles pour us vodka from bottles they keep in their armpit coat pockets.

A Christmas Carol is playing on TV, dubbed into Polish. I watch the screen or Felicia flirting with her uncles. I talk a bit to her grandmother, who knows German. I do bridge problems with Uncle Jacek, who was Warsaw junior bridge champion, but I keep forgetting the Polish numbers and suits till he gets impatient and writes them down for me on a piece of cardboard. The other uncle shows me photographs of his job site in Iraq. I doze off in a welter of boredom, drink and guilt.

It is dark when we leave and Felicia trips on the steps. I take her arm for a bit. There are no street-lights and no cars. We stand at a bus stop and Felicia leans her hip against mine, or rests her head on my arm. We get cold and she sets off, walking carefully in the middle of the road because of the pot-holes, saying she remembers the way from the year before last, but the road ends in another housing project or a place where streets are laid around overgrown vacant lots. Headlights – one bright, one dim – appear. We stand together in the middle of the road, Felicia shivering with her arms crossed under her bosom. Felicia sits in the back, but the woman who's driving talks to her through the mirror. Felicia replies shortly, with her eyes down. Once she laughs. I try to give the driver a 10-mark note but she won't have it. She gives Felicia her address, written on a bus ticket.

Popieluszko was released from prison on Christmas Eve. Felicia told me this at breakfast in the lobby. She'd had a call from Klaus Arnim at the West German Embassy, who'd had it from Glemp, the cardinal, that morning, when he called on him, just like that. It was probable that Popieluszko would preach that night at his old church by the steelworks. Felicia looked as if she'd been crying. She kept biting her lip in frustration, because tomorrow was Christmas Day and there was no edition, and by the next day everybody would have the story. It was my idea to go to the mass, I think; or maybe I just think it was my idea because Felicia made me think so. I've never known anybody, man or woman, so keen to please as Felicia Hrabek.

I wanted to be at St. Stanislaw's early, because I thought there'd be big crowds, but there were no taxis on Independence Avenue. It was raining hard, and I'd left the umbrella at Aunt Zosia's. In the end, a truck stopped for us. The driver asked Felicia about New York, where he had family, in Bayonne, New Jersey. He wouldn't take the marks either.

When I used to tell my Popieluzsko story, I said: St. Stanislaw's was full, and the crowd had spread out into the graveyard and all over a big square in front of the church. I climbed onto a wall, and then into a yew tree. Two young priests in transparent plastic surplices were stringing out cable to loudspeakers in the trees and on lamp-posts in the square. The word Solidarity ricocheted round the loudspeakers, but I couldn't tell what Popieluszko meant by it: a trades union, surely, but also something bigger and more public, like independence from Germans and Russians, and something more private, like charity. Eight months later, he was murdered. On the corner of Independence Avenue, somebody made a crib of an old Lada, with a papier mâché body in the trunk and a cross made of flowers. But this was after I'd gone back to Germany.

What I never said was this: we pushed our way into the graveyard of St. Stanislaw's. A man and a woman held an umbrella over Felicia. I wanted to count the people and so I climbed onto a brick wall and into a tree, but this made me think of something in the New Testament and so I got down. I stood in the rain while Felicia paraphrased the sermon for me. I remember nothing of it. At the end, Popieluszko began to sing and everybody joined in a carol which Felicia said went like this:

> Go to sleep, Prince Jesus
> In the kingdom of Poland

Felicia Hrabek began to cry. The crowd was moving, pushing us from umbrella to umbrella, out of the grave-yard and into the big square and then back towards Independence Avenue. I hugged Felicia to my left side. I felt her waist and bosom through her wet coat. I don't know if she was still crying, because her face and hair were soaked with rain. We reached Independence Avenue. The people filled the pavements and both lanes of the highway. Boys vaulted the crash-bars in the middle. I felt I was in a place where big events – change, history – were jostling me, like in a nineteenth-century novel.

'You must marry me, Felicia.'

'Phooey.'

'This priest can do it.'

'I'm married, for the forty-millionth time.'

'So divorce the guy.'

I don't know what Felicia was thinking, and I don't know what she would have said if she could have said it. She would probably have said 'phooey', which was a word she used a lot. A green Mercedes was stopped in the road, in among all the people, with the engine running and somebody waving at us through an open door.

I can't go on with this story. I can give you Felicia Hrabek in other places: in her car outside the Museum Koenig, her skirt on her hips; or in her bedroom in the Bleichstrasse, harrying a full wardrobe; but not running, her wet coat spreading behind her, running to Klaus Arnim's car.

FIVE

Intensity

This happened in 1984, in Kiev, on the last night of the Foreign Secretary's visit. I was in the party to look after the press, because Pat Clark was on paternity leave. The trip had been a failure and we were all getting on one another's nerves.

We were in the Hotel Ukrainiya. It was worse than anything in Moscow. The passages were dark and stank of disinfectant. Women in brown overalls stood guard at the lifts and confiscated room-keys. Meal times were unpredictable. I was working flat out in the minister's suite on his farewell speech. Once, I got away to the dining room, but the chairs had all been stacked on the tables and there was nobody about.

I hadn't eaten anything since Moscow, but I couldn't face the farewell banquet. I wanted to be on my own. All day, I called down to the concierge, begging him to find me a seat at the theatre. To my surprise, somebody slipped an envelope with a ticket for *Yevgeny Onegin* under the door. I looked forward to being alone in the Soviet Union, for the first time. With twenty minutes to go before the performance, I stood up and put on my coat.

The minister looked at me and picked up my draft of the speech. He said: 'But Richard, there's no political content. None whatever. It would be a gross error, having put across my point so forcefully in Moscow, to confine myself to . . .'

'. . . Banalities,' said Maynard. 'All right for the Germans, I suppose, but not for a UK delegation.' He was sitting with his back to the window. On a blackboard set on an easel beside his chair, somebody had written: CONVERSATIONS IN THIS ROOM ARE NOT SECRET. Maynard had his coat off. The minister had his coat off. I had seventeen minutes to get to the theatre and no Soviet money.

'Krazno is doing wheat, sir,' I said. 'My new friend at the Palace of the Republic showed me an English draft of his speech.'

'That, I am afraid, is the point, Richard. Wheat matters.' Maynard raised his voice as if for the benefit of an imaginary eavesdropper. 'We cannot afford to de-couple economic co-operation and security, whatever Anatoly Krazno does or does not do.'

'Yes, that is the point, Richard.' The minister looked tired out. I think he had no interest in theatre or, indeed, in anything outside politics. He had refused the morning's sightseeing programme. I felt I was letting him down.

'There's a reference to the force-reduction nego-tiations on page three of the draft, sir. And I've provided an alternative toast. I rather thought, as this is the private visit, and we're not in Moscow . . .'

I had twelve minutes.

'Yes, yes,' said Maynard. 'Of course, there is quite a

good chance that Krazno will be elected to the Central Committee in October.' He turned and looked out of the window.

'Yes, Richard. We must look to the coming generation of leaders.'

I said: 'I could easily re-do the draft, sir. There's a good half-hour before the delegation has to leave. And I could work during the dinner.'

'Don't you worry about it, Richard.' The minister took his pencil and made a slashing diagonal mark on the top sheet of the draft. Without looking up, he held out a page to Maynard. Maynard rose. They seemed to be waiting for me to leave the room. I hesitated and then got up and left.

I tried not to think about it. I tried to think: I have ten minutes to pick up the money in my room and get to the theatre; ten minutes for the dark passages, the interminable lift, the floor-lady, the room-keys, the passages, the floor-lady and lift again, and then a car and a driver. I am going to miss the whole first act, probably more. If only I'd brought my roubles down with me!

Maynard had no roubles. The minister had none. We hadn't needed money in Moscow. The cars that took us to the Kremlin cost nothing. The laying of wreaths cost nothing. The minister's unplanned walk in Red Square cost nothing. The flight to Kiev cost nothing. Even the opera ticket came with the compliments of the Municipality of Kiev. Only I needed money, because I was hungry.

The lift opened at last on the thirteenth floor. A lamp burned weakly on the floor-lady's desk, but there was nobody about.

'Madame! Madame!' I whispered.

'Yes.'

I turned round. Near the end of the passage, I could see the lower half of a tall woman. She was leaning against the passage wall, but her head, which was in darkness, must have almost touched the ceiling. She wore a brown overall.

'Room 1319 is open.' She spoke English with a self-assured North American accent, like the readers on Moscow Radio.

'What an angel,' I said, hurrying past her. Her feet were bare.

'No I'm not.'

My room was open. The radio was on, playing an Italian pop-song. I had nothing confidential in my luggage, and my money had been neatly piled on the bedside table, but the intrusion exasperated me.

At the other end of the passage, the woman had sat down behind her desk. She looked about thirty. Her hair was dirty and her eyes were half-closed with tiredness or boredom. The brown overall didn't help. I called the lift. After a while, her presence at my back embarrassed me.

'You speak good English,' I said.

She took such a long time to reply that I looked round. Her eyes were fully closed. She said: 'In tourist hotels, every person understands English.'

'So you know what we foreigners are up to?' I smiled to show this was a joke.

She opened her eyes. 'I also have travelled to the United Kingdom and North America.'

The lift doors opened and I escaped.

I was in luck. The delegation cars were already lined up in front of the hotel. I took the last in the line. The driver seemed to know what he was doing. We rolled past a sports stadium and along a double highway, where the tarmac glistened in the dusk. There wasn't much traffic, but the pavements were crowded with people, walking slowly as in a Mediterranean town. We came to a wide boulevard lined with steel-and-glass buildings. It seemed to end at the foot of a tall and elaborate apartment block, in the Gotham City style of some skyscrapers I'd seen in Moscow. In its shadow was a tiny, old-fashioned building covered in pink plaster. This was the theatre. The crowds were thick on the pavement, and I had to elbow and jostle my way through.

I needn't have hurried. The orchestra hadn't arrived. The theatre was half-empty. It had once been splendid. Busty caryatids supported the balconies. The seats were covered in pink velvet, though mine was black at the top from hair-oil. The scene curtain was embroidered with wheat-sheaves and the arms and initials of the Ukrainian Soviet Socialist Republic. It, too, was dirty.

My seat was the best in the house. I sat directly behind the conductor's podium. As the house filled up, four seats on each side stayed empty. Behind me were rows of middle-aged people, the men in shirt-sleeves, the women in work-dresses. The people talked through the overture. When the curtain rose, they applauded wildly, but went on talking.

It was warm in the theatre. I had been through six days of nerves and exertion. My head became intolerably heavy. I pinched my nose and cheeks. The stage blurred and rearranged itself into familiar and comfortable shapes. I bit my lip.

I woke in a gale of applause. Two old women were handing a small bouquet to the conductor.

I hurried to the exit, then made my way downstairs, where a line of people had formed. The line went on past an elaborate clock which showed the wrong time and then stretched along and around the four walls of the entrance lobby to a refreshment stand not far from where I was. Red caviar gleamed on what looked like scones. There was a big urn of tea. I waited until the bell, but the line had hardly moved. I went back upstairs, looking at signed photographs of singers. I recognized Caruso. I bought a programme and received an astonishing amount of change. The programme was in Russian and Ukrainian. I looked for a synopsis in a language I understood, but there wasn't one.

In the second act, there was a duel, which the audience applauded. Even before the curtain came down, I was out of my seat but I was caught in my exposed position as the conductor turned to take his bow. His face was shining with sweat. By the time I got away, the line was at the foot of the stairs.

The third act opened at a ball in St. Petersburg. I didn't try to concentrate. I thought of everything I had eaten in Russia. I thought mostly of a party given by Novosti for the visiting press at a magnificent house in Moscow. There was sturgeon and red and black caviar, and a sort of ravioli made with minced meat, and pancakes full of dill and sour cream and odd dishes that looked savoury and tasted sweet and the other way round. We toasted one another in vodka flavoured with lemon or pepper. One vodka tasted of honey. Another smelled of hay. By the end, the journalists were all seated on gilded chairs against the walls, shouting greetings across the devastated table.

Outside the theatre, I hesitated on the pavement. Two young men offered to help me. I brushed them off, but they persisted. They spoke English. They were students at the university, which was on the morning's tour we hadn't taken. They mentioned this, which embarrassed me. They were in the middle of their exams. When I said I wanted to go to a restaurant, they looked surprised.

The streets were still crowded. We kept coming on their classmates, some of them carrying books. The girls were pretty. They asked me and the two young men questions. I was obviously something of a catch for the boys. At moments, I was uncomfortable: the British Foreign Secretary's acting press adviser arm-in-arm with Ukrainian students. They'd told me their names but I'd forgotten them.

At last we came to a restaurant above an underground station. A porter stood in the door. His breath stank of drink. I said I was a tourist and the young men were my guests. I lost my temper. He locked the glass door in my face.

We walked to a park and sat under some chestnut trees. On other benches, soldiers and militiamen sat holding the hands of girls. There was white pollen in the air which the boys said came off poplar trees. They asked me about the British army in Northern Ireland. I asked about Afghanistan. We became heated and then calmed down. I thought it was stupid to quarrel on such a chance acquaintance and I'm sure they thought the same. We walked to a vast floodlit monument, which they said was to the dead of Babiy Yar. I asked them to join me at the hotel for tea. They were turned away at the door. We exchanged addresses but I lost theirs and they didn't write.

I went to the hotel restaurant, which was locked. I rode wearily to the thirteenth floor in the lift.

'Hello,' I said to the floor-girl. 'Is there by any chance anything to eat up here?'

She was sitting at her desk, a packet of Marlboro cigarettes and an ashtray in the light of her small lamp. She said: 'You can try the foreign currency bar on the second floor. It is open late.' Her eyes suddenly flashed: 'Do you know the group Panic? From Brescia in Italy. They're playing. They're famous in West Europe.'

'I'm sure. I was at the opera.'

'I know. *Onegin*. There were tickets for all your group but only one person went. I've never been to the opera.'

'It's good. Like London. Better.' I sat down on the edge of her desk and looked down at her long legs.

'Why do you say that when it isn't true?' She drew her legs in so they were hidden by the desk. 'And you can't sit down. You must go to the first floor. Suite 001. There was a message. Another tourist.'

I laughed. 'That's not a tourist. That's our Foreign Minister.'

'Genscher?'

'No, no. That's Germany.' I stopped laughing because I thought I was being unkind.

She seemed untroubled. 'I learn something new here every day. That's why I like to work here.'

'Will you still be here when I come back? I haven't talked with many Russians.'

'I'm not a Russian. Of course I am here. I must be here. I have your room-key.'

The lift arrived. I stepped into it and she picked up a newspaper.

'Agriculture,' said the minister, as I came in.

'The point was cleanly made on both sides,' said Maynard, stretching. 'Economic relations will survive, may even be extended, despite unbridgeable differences over security issues.'

'I entirely recast your reference to the independent deterrent, Richard,' the minister said.

'Decisively,' said Maynard. 'The emphasis was not lost on the Soviet group.'

I was having difficulty concentrating. The minister had a peculiarity of speech: he pronounced 'the' as 've'. 'Ve independent deterrent' sounded feeble. CONVER-SATIONS IN THIS ROOM ARE NOT SECRET: the chalk message gave a staginess to proceedings, as if we were performing before an empty house. Perhaps I was just hungry.

'Do you by any chance have any biscuits?'

'For God's sake, Richard,' said Maynard. He came forward from the window and made a face over the seated minister. 'I'm sorry to have dragged you down here so late, but the secretary of state has moved the programme forward. The RAF VC-10 will now leave at 8 a.m. sharp.'

'Oh,' I said. 'What about the monastery?'

'Really, Richard,' said the minister. He picked up a file and unwound the pink tape on it.

Maynard said: 'You, Richard, will be briefing them on the flight back, of course.'

'I rather thought I would go back to them for a bit before they get too pissed. But there's not a terrible lot to say. This is the private visit.'

The minister was looking closely at something in his file. Maynard looked at me. He said:

'You could go on background, couldn't you? On, say, how the Soviet side reacted to the secretary of state personally.'

I said nothing but looked, I hope, receptive to this idea.

Maynard sighed and spoke very quickly: 'There was the Defence Ministry man you mentioned in Moscow – Rostov, I believe – who was talking after the press conference. You said he used the phrase Iron Gentleman.'

'He was being sarcastic. He was furious about the Trident answer. They all were. It wasn't even meant for my hearing.'

Maynard looked at me. 'I suppose you know that for a fact, Richard.' He again raised his voice for the eavesdropper. 'My strong feeling was that despite differences, irreconcilable for the moment, over the balance of nuclear forces in Europe, the Soviets were deeply impressed by the secretary of state's clear, forthright and principled expression of the British and Nato position.'

'I'm sure that's so,' I said. 'Do you have anything to drink here?'

'I wouldn't trust the tap water,' said the minister, without looking up from his file.

'I'll rough out a few ideas before bed. Goodnight, sir, Ian.'

'Goodnight, Richard,' said Maynard. 'Krazno is coming at seven.'

It was two in the morning. I took the lift to the second floor, but the foreign-currency bar, if it had ever been open, was shut now. Through a wall of frosted and clear panes of glass, I could see artificial palm trees and a microphone and drum set.

On the thirteenth floor, the girl was still wearing her brown overall and was sitting at her desk. The newspaper had fallen to the floor. It was *Izvestiya*. She looked up with a start as I came out of the lift.

'What's Trident?' she asked.

'Our nuclear rocket. That's why we're here.' I thought: what the hell.

'Why is your negotiating position so inflexible?'

'We say the same about your side.' I sat down on the desk and smiled to show that I did not want to dispute about nuclear weapons. I felt powerful and uncontrolled.

She said: 'I found some chewing gum. Enzo of Panic gave it to me. They came up here after their concert last night.'

I took a piece, and then, because she shook the packet, a second. My jaw ached as I unwrapped each piece. The gum was very sweet.

'What's your name?'

'Helen. It's a Greek name.'

'I'm Richard.'

'My grandmother was Greek. My grandfather was Polish.'

'And you're Ukrainian?'

'No,' she said. 'There are no Ukrainians. They all died in the war. I have a son called Anton. That's Greek, too.'

'Does your husband look after him when you're working?'

She looked at me. I think she was startled by my clumsiness, rather than offended, or contemptuous. She said: 'My mother looks after Anton when I'm here. You may be tired. You should go to bed.'

'Helen, why is your English so good?'

'I said I had travelled. To England, Gatwick Airport. And New York, John Kennedy Airport. And Toronto, all over the city. I was a competitor at the three-cornered games: USA, USSR and Canada. High jump.'

She had closed her eyes.

'How high can you jump, Helen?'

'I jumped 1.85 personal best. Anton is five now.'

'Did you win at Toronto?'

She opened her eyes. I thought again that I was being too rough, that I was bruising her in some way. She said: 'You know, you should have gone to the foreign-currency bar. Panic is very well-known.'

I couldn't stop. 'Did you win in Toronto, Helen?'

She shook her head impatiently. 'It doesn't matter. My mother asks, everybody asks me, why I work here, shut up all day and night except the days off, like an animal in the ground. I could have gone back to college. My mother was an engineer. My father was a journalist. I was all-Ukraine champion for three and one-half years. But I want to meet tourists, people from other countries . . .'

'People like me? You can't mean it.'

'I do,' she said. 'You have not understood me. You travel where you wish. Moscow, Kiev: they are just cities to you. I have seen only Toronto, and it is beautiful. I had friends: Cathy, Carmel, Heather. We went everywhere. We lived with such . . . I can't express it, because English is not my second language. We lived with strength, with intenseness . . .'

'Intensity.'

'Intensity. Thank you. What time do you want your wake-up call?'

'Never.'

She looked confused, so I said: 'Six o'clock. You should sleep a bit as well, Helen. You look tired.'

'It's my job. One tourist is waking up at five o'clock. English. Maynard.'

'I know,' I said.

She offered me the rest of the gum, which I took.

I woke to the sound of a football rattle. It was my telephone ringing. Maynard was at the other end.

'Morning, Richard. I'm afraid Krazno will not be coming to the airport. We leave at once.'

'Oh God,' I said. 'I knew we should have done the sightseeing programme.'

'Don't be absurd, Richard. It's clearly a health matter. The Soviet side says that he is indisposed. There is no point hanging around. We leave in ten minutes.'

Helen had a glass of tea on her desk. In the saucer was a broken piece of sugar. She handed the glass to me. She looked more tired than ever.

'Helen, would you like this Soviet money? I don't need it any more.'

'Thank you.' She took the rouble notes and put them quickly in the desk drawer.

'We're leaving early,' I said. 'Your prime minister is displeased.'

She showed no interest, or maybe she was just too tired to show anything. I said:

'Helen, if you tell me your surname, I'll write to you from London.'

'I get postcards from tourists all the time.'

'I could send something for little Anton.'

She glanced at me, and then I knew that I had gone too far, and there was no coming back. She said: 'Thank you. He has everything.'

She stood up. I had forgotten how tall she was. She walked past me in her bare feet and called the lift, then returned to her desk and sat down.

'Don't forget to give me your key,' she said.

'I never had it.'

I got into the second car with Maynard. Motorbikes stood on each side, their engines going. Maynard was reading a telex.

'Did you get some breakfast?' he asked.

'No. I thought the secretary of state might need me.'

'No. He's with Zortin who is, quite frankly, the coming man in the Ukrainian party. Interpreters only. I could not explain over the telephone, but Krazno has a history of heart trouble. That's what prevented his election to the Central Committee in Moscow. The secretary of state is making some points we roughed out after you went to bed.'

'Oh,' I said. We were moving at high speed. Through the window, sunshine flashed on the gold dome of a church. I wished we'd seen the city in the daytime.

Maynard was speaking beside me. 'Look, Richard. I have to be brutally frank. The secretary of state is far from happy at the way the qualities have covered the visit. I have not seen the cuttings myself, but London was not encouraging.'

'It was a difficult visit.'

'Certainly. If you don't mind, Richard, I'd say you concentrated too greatly on the security issues, and not enough on the trust that the secretary of state has built up with the coming generation of Soviet leaders. Really, the very best performance I have seen from a Foreign Secretary. Pat Clark would have picked up on that.'

We were speeding through birch-woods. Militiamen were stationed at short intervals along the roadside verges. One came out of the trees, smoothing his uniform, as we passed.

'Well, there's still the in-flight briefing,' I said cheerfully.

'There is, as you say, the in-flight briefing.'

The airport terminal was a long, low building of 1950s vintage. It looked like something out of *Tintin*. The press bus was already at the entrance. The journalists were straggling through different control posts. At the back, sweating, was Alan Bristow of the *Daily Telegraph*. He was carrying two large plastic bags and searching clumsily through his raincoat pockets for something. He was also hampered by a cigarette.

I liked him very much. This was not because he was reliable. He wasn't. I liked him, I think, because he made such heavy weather of life. He wrote beautifully, but he stuttered and got bogged down if he asked a question at a briefing. He seemed perpetually anxious about what other journalists were writing. I tapped him on the back. He jumped.

'Ah, Richard,' he said with relief.

'Do you want me to carry one of your bags through duty free at Heathrow? It's just one more worry, isn't it.'

'I hate diplomats,' he said. 'Thank you very much.'

He had found what he was looking for: a currency form. He handed it to a lady in uniform. She waved me through but I waited for Bristow, and we joined the next queue.

He said: 'Bit of a blow about Krazno, eh? The last straw, isn't it, Richard?'

'I'm lost, old fellow. Come again.'

'I mean, rather a snub, isn't it? I mean, not coming to see the Foreign Secretary off. Here.'

'Oh, I see what you mean. I never thought of that. Well, I suppose . . . You do know, Alan, that he's on a dialysis machine. We never expected him to come.'

'Yes,' said Bristow firmly. I never met a journalist who liked to admit he didn't know something. 'Still, the visit hasn't been the greatest success, has it?'

'Depends how you look at it.' I spoke quickly. 'If you seriously expected that in six days a UK Foreign Secretary could achieve a breakthrough on arms control and secure the peace of Europe for a generation, you have to be a little disappointed. Actually, we're rather chuffed – and not just about the co-operation agreements. Moscow . . .' I broke off.

Bristow was not trying to find something else, but he turned half-round to face me. 'Go on, Richard.'

'On background?'

'On background.'

'All right. It's more sentiment than substance – and that's what matters in diplomacy. Who cares about wheat and student exchanges.' I paused again. 'Did you by any chance meet Marshal Bezukhov?'

'Mmmm.' Most journalists find it just as hard to admit they don't know somebody.

'For God's sake, don't use his name or mine or I'll never speak to you or your newspaper again. Bezukhov came up to me, after the first round in the Kremlin, and said, quite without prompting, that despite the Trident issue, he was impressed. We were talking English. He said he was impressed by the secretary of state's . . . by the secretary of state's . . .'

Bristow disappeared into a booth, and a curtain was drawn behind him. I heard the clatter of things falling to the ground: coins mostly and something heavy, perhaps a cigarette lighter.

'Intenseness,' I said loudly so he could hear. 'That was the word he used. Intensity, really.'

I showed my passport and sidestepped the booth. On the other side, Bristow had a pen out and he was writing on his cigarette packet.

I felt hot and tired, though it was not yet eight in the morning.

*

Soon after the Soviet trip, I left the Foreign Office and went into the City. I kept meaning to go back to Kiev, to see the place. Then I went to New York and Chernobyl happened, and it became impossible.

SIX

Christmas in New York

One Monday in December, 1985, I had a letter from my mother, though she'd been dead eighteen years. It was wedged in the keyboard of my Telerate machine in the dealing room at Murchison Steinman. Past the machine and past the starlings on the ledge and the bare white trees of Central Park, the windows of the Century were ablaze with early sun.

The address was in black ink: italic, done with a fountain pen, the handwriting of an artist or art student, a woman, English. I closed my eyes and saw an Edwardian hat, a faded Chinese dressing-gown and a woman's warm, round back, a little creased from the rumpled sheet.

I put the letter in the desk drawer and immediately took it out again. It was as if Angelica had walked right in, sat on the desk and got out her cigarettes, as she'd done once in the library of the Oriental Institute. I felt longing for Angelica, shame, anxiety – authentic and inseparable sensations from the summer of 1977 in Oxford – , and guilt about Billy, her father. I hadn't seen him or written to him since before Kuwait. I thought: if I marry Anne Keenan, we'll ask them both though I don't see him getting to New York let alone Louisville, Kentucky, he must be getting on.

I opened the envelope with my fingernail and shook it upside down. An air-mail sheet fell out. I shook it again and an envelope fell on the keyboard, folded, grey with age, with an English stamp from years ago and my mother's beloved handwriting.

I think of this moment often. I try to set out my feelings in order of their appearance and intensity. I know I felt such terror I might have been tumbling down the cold chasm of 61st Street. I thought: ah, so she didn't die in Kettering General or died but didn't lose consciousness; and all I've done since then she's seen and understood; and all these things around me – the stock quote machines and flashing phones, the blind wall of the Pierre, the ducting of the Metropolitan Club, the threadbare trees, the skaters circling the Wollman Rink, the sirens and rumbling trucks, the faint Christmas carols from the GM building – are not the result of uncountable choices and accidents but are as they only could be; and God is up there in miles of blue heaven; and I was flooded with such relief that tears jumped from my eyes.

I don't know if I saw the stamp first, or the envelope or my mother's handwriting, because I was used at school to see them all in an instant, after lunch, filing out of the dining room and past the long sideboard where the letters were spread out; and there, right at the end, something would quiver into life and I would push and jostle because it was so intimate with its my darling Richard and all my love Ma that I couldn't bear the others to see it; as if it were the very feel of my

72

mother, her green jumper, the crackle of her skirt and hair, her bosom, the scent of Ormonde by Floris.

I suspect I saw the stamp first. It was upside down on the keyboard but I could see by its colours – burnt siena, crimson lake – that this was the 3d. commemorative issue for the World Postal Union Congress in Birmingham, 5–7 February, 1967, with two phosphor bands and a catalogue value of – I didn't know the catalogue value.

The stamp tripped unimportant sensations: the sharpness of a stamp hinge on my tongue or an ache in my neck at the end of an afternoon propped over a stamp album on the floor. These were swept away in a rush of escaping time. Nineteen sixty-seven engulfed me. I saw my first hippie and smelled again the smell of the squash court where I did my scholarship. The hospital reared up out of the wet car park like a factory. The tall brick chimney terrified me. Rubber doors pushed open and enveloped me. Smells of medicine or gas; the roar of a generator somewhere; my mother's bed against a pillar the colour of chocolate and a woman speaking into a pay-phone all the time, all the time.

The tide went down. I saw I held an envelope of the cheap sort my mother used, addressed to Billy in her difficult handwriting. I went to boarding school when I was seven and my mother died when I was twelve. I suppose I knew my mother's handwriting better than my mother. She joined letters together and sometimes words, but I could pull them apart. I could tell an *n* from an *a* or an *e*, and a *p* from a *g*. (Is this where I learned the patience to read manuscript Persian?) I could read my mother's writing even now, when the lines of the address dipped to the right and the letters were all misshapen, as if she were drunk or writing with her right hand instead of her left.

I put both letters in the drawer. I looked at the Tele-rate screen. I'd like to say I remember that Fed Funds traded at $7^{17}/_{32}$ and the dollar was firm and the long bond up $^1/_{16}$ but I can't. I went off for my meeting with Jack Steinman but he'd cancelled. I opened Angelica's letter:

26 Leighton Road
London NW5

10 December, 1985

Dear Ricky

I'm sorry I didn't get in touch with you earlier,
but as you can guess it's been just chaotic here.
Billy was cremated at Northampton, just like Ma,
which is what they both wanted, and afterwards
everybody came back to No. 11 and we had quite
a party, he would have enjoyed it. Your sister
Amanda came, I haven't seen her for years. She
said you'd become a stockbroker, you Fascist!

While I was going through Billy's letters, I
found this one which I thought you might like
to have.

With love

Angelique

I sat at the screen till the market closed. At intervals, I thought of Billy. At ten past four, I rode down in the elevator with the mail clerks. My mother's letter felt powerful and atrocious in my coat pocket, as I imagine a handgun feels. The sky over the park was still blue. It was bitter cold. I felt so light with hunger and strangeness that I thought I might float away. On the corner of 59th Street, a Volunteer of America stood in a Santa Claus uniform, ringing a bell. From the astroturfed court at the base of the GM building, 'Jingle Bells' rang out from under a silver sleigh.

I went to the Hellas at 59th Street and Madison Avenue, paused for a moment in the hot blast from the radiator above the door, sat down at the counter. The old man put down a large orange juice.

'BLT on wholewheat down for the gentleman!'

A woman in a black fur coat on my left fidgeted with her Bloomingdales shopping bags. On the far side of the counter, the old man's daughters moved up and down. They neither touched nor spoke. Their aproned hips communicated intolerable tension.

My plate had gone. In its place was a cup of black coffee and a slim hand pushing back the perspex hood above the muffins.

'No. Not today.'

I looked into her brown eyes but she looked straight back so I turned away. I felt hurried, hemmed in, sticky from the sandwich which seemed to have kept its shape in my stomach, hot from the radiator above the door and the fur coats on each side. I reached down into my coat and got out my mother's letter.

10 February, 1967

My darling Billy

I'm writing this with my right hand so you'll just have to lump it. I get tired so I'll do the business side first. Marjorie came this morning, with a draft will. I'd like you very much, Billy, if you can bear it, to be Ricky's guardian. It won't mean anything financial, or at least not from you. His father obviously hasn't got anything but Marjorie gathers that the old lady can be stung till he leaves school. The headmaster thinks he should sit the Cranford scholarship, though they're all buggers these prep-school masters, aren't they, so how can you tell?

P.M.
Ricky has just left with Amanda and John for the station. I feel ghastly skiving off like this. Amanda got sanctimonious and said if I hadn't gone to lunch with you, I wouldn't have been on the by-pass then but if I hadn't gone out to see your wretched *h. orientalis* I might have been all right all the same! I hope Ricky will understand, and your poor Muriel too, and even God, though I don't suppose He's that interested.

I've made myself cry, it's the stuff they're giving me. Please do the Ricky thing, Marjorie will sort it all out,

With all my love

Kate

'More coffee?'

'Check.'

Beside me, the lady in the fur coat slides off her stool, juggling her parcels. The waitress slaps down her pad. At my left, a black-leather arm moves across the counter and drops two small things of gold into the waitress's hand: earrings, Tiffany earrings. I'd seen them in the shop, in the big case nearest the Fifth Avenue entrance, when I was looking for an engagement ring. The waitress turns round, picks up a bagel and cuts it in two, puts down the two halves and then the knife. She turns and her oval face is red all over and her eyes are sparkling. She picks up the pad, lets it flop down again on the counter, start totting up figures and then forgets, looks at me and then out of the window where a young man with a pig-tail, a leather jacket and a pink nylon knapsack – is he the guy? – is walking past. She looks back down at the pad, smiling to herself, starts to count again, steps back and tries to catch her sister's eye (who doesn't want to know), then comes forward again and looks at me for some complicity, an understanding of what it is to be eighteen or nineteen, and gets instead the look men give her all day, every day.

(For I was there one Saturday night, at The Tunnel downtown! And that was my apartment where your Sunday just kind of vanished; and I once heard a girl shriek, Jesus, it's seven already, and clatter down the four-and-a-half flights; and saw her running to 14th Street and smelled the lovely smell of sex rising from her lap to fill the uptown subway car; and then lay back and smoked another cigarette and, leaning right across to stub it out, saw, on the packing-crate beside the bed, a pair of Tiffany earrings!)

'Shit. I can't do this.'

'I can. It's $4.40. Take 5.'

The cold makes my forehead ache. My leather soles ring out on the sidewalk like hammers. I turn on to 57th Street and join a stream of people pushing towards Fifth Avenue till we are stopped by the light opposite Tiffany's.

(I should have known my mother might fall in love, alone, divorced, broke, with two children; and why not Billy, a neighbour, who loved painting, gardens and facetious jokes?)

In front of Tiffany's the crowd loses its purpose, begins to swirl and eddy like leaves in a draughty court-yard.

(But how could I have known at Studland, up on the shingle, by the breakwater, a man with an easel and a Frenchman's hat and my mother saying: Can that be Billy up there? Or driving back to school, by Morvern Sands, a car broken down and Look! It's Angelica and Billy, she in a brown velvet hairband. And Billy's sup-posed to be coming some time, staying at the Hydro, doing some painting.)

St. Pat's. Saks, where I give a dollar to the blind man with the dog. Down the sidestreets come fire engines and grit. Tears chill my cheeks. At Lord & Taylor, the crowds are four deep at the velvet ropes to see the Christmas windows. The clock at Altman's says 5.25. I'm in good time for Anne, who's coming straight from the clinic.

(I do not understand. If love can call my mother back

78

to tell me this, it can upend the Empire State or exchange its floodlit tower for the moon riding over my right shoulder. If love can bring my mother back to life, there is nothing love cannot do. If love can bring my mother back to life, why must she die again?)

This is the second half of my life. This is 23rd Street. There are no crowds here. Fifth Avenue runs down to Washington Square. I can see the floodlit arch. I can see the traffic lights turn green, block by block.

SEVEN

Slide

The second summer we lived in New York, we rented a house upstate to go to at weekends. We shared it with Ed Stark and Miriam Gross. Anne knew her from Vassar.

It took us April and May to find the place. We started looking on the east end of Long Island, because Ed knew somebody, another photographer, whose girlfriend did real estate in Bridgehampton. She was called Inge. We met her on Easter Sunday in a café that smelled of ice-cream and lard. Men in windcheaters sat at a long counter, each one reading the *New York Times*. A little girl blew bubbles in a pink milk-shake.

'Did you see Mort Jablonsky?' said Inge as we got up into her land-cruiser.

'Who's he?'

She giggled: 'I don't know.'

We looked also in Sag Harbor and Montauk. We spent the next two weekends on the Jersey shore. Anne went to Bucks County, Pennsylvania. We saw a place near Kent, Connecticut, with a pond and a boat with a hole in it, but it was $5,000 for the season. In Darien,

Connecticut, at a gas station under a ramp to Route 84, I punched a phone box.

Anne didn't see this. She sat in her coat in the hire car. She said: 'Why can't Ed and Miriam look?'

'She's got a closing.'

'Ed hasn't.'

I left a message for Ed downtown. The telephone woke me on Monday morning. It was Connie, who worked for Miriam at Goldman Sachs.

'It's a farm, or was,' I said to Anne. 'With views of Slide Mountain. $1500 for the season.'

Anne was facing the wall. She said: 'Is it above ground? Does it have a roof? Is it, like, kind of funky?'

I kissed her neck. She sat bolt upright in bed. She said: 'Are Ed and Miriam coming to see it?'

'Of course they are.'

We drove out together on the Saturday of the Memorial Day weekend. It was raining. We took the Palisades to Bear Mountain, then turned west on Route 17. Trucks blinded the windscreen with spray. We passed farms with broken-down silos and fields gone over to grass or scattered with resort billboards. Anne kept looking down at directions she'd written on an envelope.

Route 17 came into a narrow valley. The road crossed and recrossed a stream on concrete stilts. We took exit 97, which doubled back under the highway and over the swollen stream and then turned to dirt. At intervals, the trees on each side had been hacked away to make room for trailers.

The track climbed into dark hemlock firs. Water poured down the middle of it, the colour of melted milk chocolate. Ed had the Sunday sections of the *New York Times*. Miriam was asleep.

'Richard!'

'I am being fucking careful!'

Anne looked back down at Connie's directions.

'Richard! Here, left here.'

The firs fell back behind the car. The track turned up to the left. Grass fields ran off into fog on both sides. My eyes ached with the brightness. The track went on to a red barn and, past it, a small house with white metal or plastic siding and two trees that looked like maples arching above it. A man was sitting in an idling pick-up.

Miriam was awake. 'Well done, little Connie,' she said.

It rained the first two weekends. Our bed was hard and sloped steeply towards Anne. I kept waking early and thinking I would see a mountain filling the screened window. When I got up to look, I couldn't see past the barn for rain. Blackbirds with red patches on their wings shrieked from a telephone wire. Anne was always awake, with a nightgown on and two jumpers, reading. Miriam was in San Francisco. Ed was on a shoot.

They came in the middle of June. It was hot, in the nineties, but cloudy. I picked them up on Saturday afternoon at Port Jervis station.

'Great car,' Ed said, thumping the bonnet of the Impala.

'$500. Hoos Auto Body. Livingston Manor.'

'You overpaid, dummy,' said Miriam.

At the farm, Anne was cleaning the pans in the

kitchen. Ed walked past her to the stove, twisted a dial and looked at me pityingly.

'Dick. You should have told me it's not gas.'

'I should have told you a lot of things.'

I woke up when it was still dark. Anne was reading.

'Maybe they won't come much,' she said.

'Oh, they're OK.'

'They don't do anything together.'

Ed spent his time cooking. His actions were precise, maybe even fussy. I liked the way he slid his bread dough off the board he was working on, put a plate on top, then dried his hands on his handkerchief. Miriam talked to New York on the telephone, or slept on the orange sofa or read a big paperback. At dinner, she ate a bowl of cold cereal and drank Coke.

Anne said: 'I'm having a baby.'

'Anne!'

'I had the thing the day you were in Pittsburgh. I wanted to be sure.'

On Sunday morning, the sky was blue but there was no mountain in the window. The grass fields ran off the hill and then there were woods, rising and falling away into the haze. The owner was doing something in the barn, his pick-up engine running. His name was Jake.

'We're going for a swim,' Anne said when we walked past.

'I got the screen-door,' he said. 'Just needs fixing up.'

We were at the stream when I looked back and saw Ed and Miriam waving from the house.

'Got to see our property,' said Ed, coming up.

We followed the stream up into woods. I put leaves

in my pocket to identify from the book later. Anne went first, jumping carefully from side to side of the stream to find the easiest way. It was too hard going to talk.

We came after a while to a concrete slipway clogged with brambles and, at the top of it, a dam holding in a small lake. The lake gleamed with dust in the sunshine. Anne breasted her way through mountain laurel which grew all along the dam. Frogs squeaked and jumped in as we passed.

'It's better the far side for swimming,' I said. 'Where the stream comes in.'

I waded out. The water was cold but there was gravel under foot. I walked out further.

'It's wonderful, guys.'

Something crawled up my leg and I took a step forward. Something else ran up the inside of my leg till it reached my swimming shorts. I sprang forward and began to swim, my neck stiff, my head aching with cold.

'It's wonderful.'

I turned on my back to watch Anne. I knew what she would do. She was going to take two steps, lean forward, put her hands between her legs just above the knee, shiver and shout something rude at me. Then she was going to push out, flailing her arms and blowing.

'You bastard! It's freezing!'

I looked up at blue sky. The trees grew all round the lake to the same height, like a big fence. I felt dizzy with pleasure. I dived under and swam through the murk towards Anne.

'Dick!' Ed was shouting from the bank. Miriam was looking at us over her shoulder. 'We should get back. The venison. See you.'

'We're coming.'

By the stream was the remains of a track, with a thick grass verge in the middle. It looked as if it might take us back. I walked with Ed.

'We should climb Slide,' I said.

Ed had his head down.

'It's the mountain you're supposed to see from the farm. Jake says there's nothing to see from the top so its sure to be worth it.'

Ed patted me on the back. 'We just got here, man.'

Ed and Miriam didn't come again until the 4th July weekend. We went up all together in the Impala on Thursday evening, to beat the traffic. We didn't. Something dragged on the ground and I stopped on the Palisades.

'It's the muffler,' Ed said. 'It doesn't matter.'

On Route 17, there were old American cars all over the shoulders and median. Hasidic Jews struggled with bursting luggage on their roof-racks. A boy bustled through the lanes of slow traffic, his black waistcoat flapping. We stopped at Monticello, to break the journey for Anne, though I didn't say this to Ed and Miriam.

At the farm, there was still no screen-door. Two men came in the morning to cut the hay. Goldfinches darted in front of the mower. Miriam lay in shorts on the orange sofa, weeping with hay fever.

'Even your mountain must be better than this,' she said.

We set off for Slide after lunch on Saturday. The Impala wouldn't start.

'Roll it down the hill and start it,' Ed said. 'Why not?'

The trailers were giddy with flags. One had small flags in thirteen rows across its lawn.

'The American dream,' Miriam said. She had a small lisp, which made her sound ironical sometimes.

'What is the American dream, Miriam?'

'Don't, Richard,' Anne said.

'I mean: what does it mean? I really want to know and nobody will bloody tell me.' I banged the steering wheel.

'Richard! For God's sake!'

A man on a motorbike was coming up at me. I stood on the brake. The Impala drifted to the left. I was relieved we were not going to hit the man. He put his bike down on its left side, hopped out from under it and fell over. We were going to hit a tree.

I was sorry we wouldn't get up Slide and the car would be no good to get us back to the city and the $500 was lost. Ed was making himself into a ball beside me. I thought then I would be injured and I thought of Anne and our baby.

We hit the tree, which was a maple. There were these sounds: breaking headlamp glass, branches scratching against metal, dirt and stones hitting the bottom of the car, Anne crying. Then there was just a creaking sound, which was the starred windscreen.

My door had fallen off so I got out. The steering wheel was bent into a square. Ed was outside, trying to put the ear-piece back on his glasses. Behind him, a man in a red tracksuit and a stars-and-stripes top hat was pounding up the road. Behind him was a woman in a pink bathrobe. The motorbike rider was sitting with his legs wide apart on the ground.

I pulled at my seat to help Anne out. It wouldn't budge. She was low down and her right leg was under the seat to the knee. The big man in the tracksuit pulled me out of the way and lifted Anne out, as one would spaghetti from a pot. He put her down in some day-lilies beside Miriam, who had her head bowed down in her lap. It was much hotter than the farm. The road flickered in the heat of a grill fire. I smelled meat.

'Your face is bleeding,' I said to Ed.

'So's yours.'

The tracksuit man came back to stand with us. We all looked at the car bonnet, which had buckled up into a peak. I put my hand in my pocket and pulled out leaves.

'Been drinking?'

'Skid,' I said.

'A skid,' Ed said.

The woman was kissing Anne.

'I said go call the ambulance, May.'

'I'm helping this lady. Are you blind?'

The man bellowed at her. Ed jumped. The woman jogged off, and then walked.

Anne had her right shoe off. Her ankle was swollen. I started to roll up her trouser, but she pushed me off. When I looked up, a police cruiser was askew across the road.

'You been drinking?' The officer stood very close to me.

'I had one glass of red wine.'

'In this weather.' He leaned back to say this, and everybody laughed, including me. He was much younger than us.

An ambulance was bumping up the road. Its light flashed thinly in the sunshine. Miriam still had her head bowed but her right hand was above her, holding on to Ed's.

'Excuse me, officer.' I walked back towards Anne.

He touched me on the sleeve. 'Hold on, pal. They'll get to you in good time. Where were you all headed all together?'

A paramedic was helping Anne into the ambulance. Another came up to me, shone a flashlight in both my eyes, washed something off my lip with a cloth and then gently lifted the front of my shirt.

'Nice,' the policeman said.

'He's OK,' the nurse said.

I rode with the officer back up to the farm to get the car papers and then down to Liberty hospital. The Impala looked as if it had been there for years, except for welts on the road. Anne's shoulder bag was in the lilies.

The rest of the day is a bit fuzzy. I remember standing in the hot parking lot, holding a Coke the policeman had given me from a cooler in his trunk. I didn't know where to put it down. Anne's bed was closed off by a curtain. In the next cubicle, I saw a black man's bare ankle cuffed to the bed. Some men were in there with him, two or even three of them.

One said: 'Did you eat, man? You want a pizza? A cup of coffee?'

It was quiet for a bit, then somebody said: 'What did you go doing that for, on a day like this?'

I remember also somebody shouting something over and over on a loudspeaker and Anne's curtain blowing out at me and a woman nurse, with I ♥ Liberty Nurses on a badge on her bosom, scrambling and scraping on the polished floor, her arms out, her white shoes struggling to get a grip till she lunged at my shoulder and pulled herself up and ran past me and out into the corridor.

Anne had her right foot bandaged. Her face was white.

'You left your bag.'

She smiled.

'I'm sorry, Anne.'

'You can't do anything.'

A taxi took us back to the farm. It cost $45. Ed had two bottles of champagne in brown bags. The next day, my head ached and my chest hurt from the steering-wheel bruises. I made Anne a bag of ice for her foot but she couldn't keep still, lying sometimes on the sofa, sometimes in her hammock, sometimes on her stomach in the grass. I thought we might be all right, but while Ed was making dinner I followed Anne into the bed-room and she said she was bleeding.

I thought that Anne wouldn't want to go to the farm again, but the city was hot as hell and I think the apartment got on her nerves. Ed and Miriam stayed with the share till Labor Day, but we kept it right on until the start of hunting season, when Jake said he could let the place for $1,000 a week to hunters. It got cold and the trees dropped their leaves and I could see Slide quite well just to the right of the barn, but I didn't mention going again. Our last weekend, Jake fitted the screen door which made Anne laugh out loud.

We stayed in New York another year. The strange thing is that when I think about America now, I don't think much about the city or work or the beautiful places we went to after we gave up the farm, like Maine. I see Jake going in and out of the barn, and Miriam asleep on the orange sofa, and Anne by the lake, drying her hair with a towel, and then crying, crying, crying.

EIGHT

Edith Kessler

When I think of Edith Kessler, I have this picture of her. She is coming slowly towards me down the grass lane from the gate to the Matamoros road, wearing a washed-out blue dress to her knees and sandals but no stockings. She is carrying a string bag. On her right is a red hibiscus hedge. On her left is the back half of her grey Volkswagen beetle. Above her are the amazing cliffs of Agua Fria.

I am sitting on her patio in the sunshine, reading the Penguin *Conquest of New Spain* or playing with Katherine. Edith doesn't see me. Her eyes are down. She seems absorbed or maybe she isn't thinking at all but conserving her strength in the way animals are supposed to do in hibernation. I call and she jumps, waves her left hand, smiles, shouts.

I don't know how old Edith Kessler was when we stayed with her in Ague Fria in 1987. I didn't feel I could ask her. She said she rode from El Paso, Texas, to Matamoros in 1929, the year the stock market crashed, and that was after her first divorce from Peterson so she must have been twenty or at least in her late-teens then.

I know some things about Edith quite well because she talked about them over and over again: the time she was in Reno and lost Peterson's ring at craps, or the disastrous trip to Moscow with Kessler and André Malraux. But these are episodes. Kessler's book mentions her on the second to last page but that came out in 1955, the year before he died. The 1960s and 1970s are a blank. I don't know when she met Buso von Berens, or if they were married.

Anne couldn't stand this. She likes biographies and conversation to advance from established premises to believable conclusions. We might be sitting, at breakfast on the patio maybe, with Buso there, and Edith saying:

'Of course, he had the biggest penis in Chestnut Hill.'

'Who had, Edith? Who?'

But Edith was off on her story, and Anne could only hang on, interrupting when she could, till Edith looked up again, startled and a bit cross, and said:

'Why, Peterson, of course. He drank a pint of Jack Daniels every day we were married.'

I'm surprised they became friends. There was the age thing, and Edith showed no interest in the clinic and kept forgetting what Anne did. I never saw her pick up or hold Katherine. I think she guarded her Bohemianism. Once I came back with her from the Friday market in the plaza and Anne was in the kitchen, warming a bottle of milk in a big kettle on the fire.

'What are you doing that for?' Edith's voice was deep, a bit nasal. Her vowels were long. I think this was an upper-class Philadelphia accent of sixty years ago, or maybe it was just Edith.

Anne explained what she was doing.

Edith sat down on a chair askew at the table. She poured herself a quarter of a glass of wine. She said: 'I had Nadia in Barcelona. I was reading *Time* magazine and she just sort of . . .' Edith opened her palms and dropped them.

'Macho, Edith,' said Anne, with her back to us.

We met Edith in New York, through a West German at the United Nations I'd known in Bonn. I asked her about Kessler and she clapped her hands in pleasure. Later she phoned to invite us to lunch. Her apartment was on West 43rd Street. It had one room the width of two outstretched arms and a kitchen with a bath in it. Both rooms were full of people. She paid $40 a month, which was one-thirty-second of our rent on Grand Street.

She was obviously broke, but she got somehow to Agua Fria each Christmas and for most of the summer. I think she may have got some money from Germany. A man at Marburg University had done a documentary on Kessler for Hessische Rundfunk. He sent a videotape of it to Edith in New York and I was supposed to translate it for her, but she kept interrupting while it was playing. The Marburg man was doing a new edition of Kessler's book, which he wrote in French after Buchenwald with Malraux doing an introduction. Somebody told Edith she might get a pension from Bonn, as the widow of a victim of National Socialism, and I promised to look into it but never did.

She once said she got no money from Buso, not one red peso.

When I picture Buso von Berens, he is walking away from me down the narrow path between the wall of

Gamba's villa and the stream. He has on a black beret, askew, a faded red-striped jacket, muddy trousers rolled up above his skinny ankles, plastic shoes and no socks. He carries a stick.

Buso is ahead of me, because we can't walk abreast. Gamba has put broken glass in his wall and we keep coming on places where the floods have washed chunks out of the path, though Buso's men have mended it with concrete and chicken wire. There are big trees of the kind called *atahuete* and they keep out a lot of sunlight. Garbage lies in drifts on the river corners.

I don't know how old Buso is, either. The date I can fix with him is January, 1933, because that was when Hitler came to power and Buso said he walked out of the German Embassy in Washington, took a cab to the Union station and then the Zephyr to Santa Fe. I'm sure he was at least in his thirties then, to be first secretary in such an important German embassy.

From a distance, Buso seems to be hanging on to life by just a thread. He halts and turns to me and I catch up with him. He is in a patch of sunlight. He is smiling. He points with his stick and says: 'An unfortunate cow was borne down in the flood. She lay with her legs in the air on Gamba's lawn for a month while he prosecuted a lawsuit in Matamoros. The smell was terrible.' He rolls his 'r's dramatically. Prosecute. Matamoros. Terrible.

We follow Gamba's wall till it ends at a point where two branches of the Atocha meet. Buso calls them the Mosel and the Rhein, and the place where they meet Kaiser Dreieck. Here he has built his biggest dam, but it is March and the pool is almost dry and rotten fruit and plastic bottles of cooking oil peer out of the mud.

On one end of the dam is a plaster-of-Paris statue of the Virgin of Guadalupe and a sign in Spanish which says: 'Do not throw garbage in the reflection of Our Lady.' We sit down in a damp concrete bandstand with a roof of green corrugated iron.

He says: 'I erected this to seat the diplomatic corps.'

At the villa, Edith is making guacamole, which she does badly. I can sense Anne's fingers itching. Edith says: 'What on earth do you want to go and see his stupid dams for?'

'Buso's amazing, Edie. You never said.'

'He's a remarkable man. All alone, he is showing these people how to conserve their groundwater.' She stops and then says: 'Kessler hated him.'

Anne turns round and settles Katherine on her hip.

Edith says: 'When Kessler died, I had $3 in my pocket and I didn't know anybody in La Paz. Of course, they wouldn't let him into America because of the McCarthy thing. I had to call Peterson collect in Palm Springs and he said I could have $50 by Western Union, that was all I was worth. Peterson was like that.'

'Edith,' Anne says. 'You were talking about Buso.'

Edith sits down. I take over the guacamole.

She says: 'Without that river, he'd die.'

Our visit was not a success. Anne fussed that Katherine might get ill. We always seemed to be boiling water, which took hours because of the altitude. I found meals difficult. Buso had special things of his own: a plastic cup of milk, half a tortilla spread with honey. Edith would be laying the things on the patio and then forget what she was doing, or start telling a story, or sit down and close her eyes. Buso sat at the table in the sunshine, chewing his lips before an empty place.

Lunch we always had out, at other houses in Agua Fria. We met a man whose father had owned the bull-ring in Matamoros; a maddening Frenchwoman who had sat for Balthus as a child; a stockbroker who wore riding breeches; a former *Newsweek* correspondent with an Italian wife; and other people though not, of course, Gamba because of the row over the dams.

Everybody made a fuss of Buso. I remember at one lunch, in the garden of the bull-ring man's, Anne and I were placed on each side of Buso. She asked him something I didn't hear.

He said: 'I came to Matamoros and saved von Humboldt's house for posterity. They were using it for chickens. I picked up great handfuls of his botanical papers from the hutches.' (I hear him now rolling the 'r' in great.)

'So you knew Edith before the war?'

'Oh, no, Anne.' Edith leaned across me. 'Nobody knew Buso then. People like Tom Fickling wouldn't see him. Everybody thought he was a spy.'

The bull-ring man's handsome face creased in a frown. He was wearing no shirt, just a silver crucifix. He put his hand firmly on Edith's.

Anne frowned. 'A spy for who, Edith?'

Edith shook off the bull-ring man's hand. Her cheeks were red. 'I don't know. For them. For the Nazis. Kessler always thought so.'

'Nonsense, Edith,' I said.

Buso was turned gallantly towards Anne, and still talking about chickens, because he was saying something about a cockerel and a coral snake. I think they were fighting in the yard of the Humboldt house. I had Katherine on my lap. Other people were talking. After a while, I looked up and Edith had lost her colour.

Our last morning, I went out with Buso after breakfast to see the damage. Gamba's people had broken down the weir at Kaiser Dreieck. Three Indian men were waiting for us with shovels and a hod of cement. They took off their caps when I shook their hands. I had a hangover or something wrong with my stomach because the garbage made me sick.

'They break my hydraulics,' Buso said. 'They throw basuras. Yet I will pursue my project. *Der gute Soldat.*'

'Were you a soldier, Buso?'

'Oh yes,' he said. He stopped and turned round. 'In Dresden, I was a cadet, in the prince's personal bodyguard. Each Sunday, we rode through the city to the Garrison Church. How we rattled and clattered!'

I felt Buso was as light as air and he was going to float up over the big trees. He said: 'At the door of the church, our colonel shouted the command: "Helmets off! For prayer!" '

I felt the river fall away and the cliffs of Agua Fria, and Matamoros and Latin America, and enough years for several lifetimes, and Hitler and Stalin and Joe McCarthy and Tom Fickling, and me and Anne not listening to each other and Katherine married to some jerk and the three Indians sleeping under their gardens. Buso lifted his stick above his head and shouted into the big trees: '*Leibeskuerassiere! Helme ab! Zum Gebet!*'

NINE

Silas Marner

I was fired by Murchison Steinman on 20 October, 1987, the day after the stock market crashed. We kept the apartment on Grand Street till the end of the month, then put our things into store. Anne's travel agent had a cancellation, a place in Barbados we could take for five weeks. Anne wanted a holiday. I wanted to think.

On the way down, Katherine caught a cold. The first evening at Mullins, she screamed in her bath, tried to scramble out. I had dinner alone, listening to her choke on her screams upstairs. Moths flew out of the darkness and chinked against the glass shades of the hurricane lamps. At one in the morning, Anne came to bed, her hair unbrushed. She lay beside me, rigid with rage. I got up without saying anything, put on some shorts and closed the door quietly behind me.

Between our rooms was a passage, which opened to a balcony. The floor was of unpolished board still warm from the day. Upright against my shoulder, head under my chin, Katherine sobbed. I walked twelve steps up and twelve steps down. Her breathing slowed, became easier. Twice I laid her gently in her cot but she cried and held on to my neck. I walked twelve steps up and twelve back, with the door to the balcony half-open and, every now and then, a breath of damp wind on my chest.

On my left, coming from Katherine's room, were these things: a collapsible wooden stool for holding a suitcase; a mahogany side-table with four drawers and, on it, a hurricane lamp with a spotted glass shade; a Spy cartoon of a man in a checked Norfolk jacket and a Derby hat; a mahogany french door with a white metal grille over the glass; a mahogany chair with a yellow velvet seat, rather dirty; a mahogany-framed double map of St. Vincent and Barbados, badly foxed (though I can just make out Mullins among places called Williams, Austin, Woodbridge, Chuse and Alleyne or with names that might have been titles of Donne poems: The Risk, The Whim, The Point); a second french window, with one door and one of its white jalousies half-open onto the red floor of the balcony and through it a coral balustrade, the top of a frangipani tree, a swing-seat before a chapel with a red-tiled roof, banana trees, palms, sugar canes and the sun coming up the colour of gold; another chair with a yellow velvet seat; a big mahogany chest of drawers with pieces of veneer missing and, above it on the wall, a map with the inscription:

Novissima et Acuratissima
Barbados
Descriptio
per
Johannem Ogilvium
Cosmographum Regium

on a shield in the bottom right-hand corner; (here

Mullins isn't marked and all the place-names are along the coasts – Sixmen Bay, W. Painter, Coll. Bayleys Well, Reads Bay – while the empty interior of the island is filled out with drawings of crop plants: a palm (marked 'A Cabage tree'), a stalk of Indian corne, Pappaw tree, Bennawna, A Pine Aple, Sugar Cane and a picture of four black men grinding cane between two big mill-stones); then another folding stool for luggage with Katherine's rattle on it and on the wall above a framed print entitled 'A West India Sportsman' and showing a plain stretching towards sketchy mountains and, in the foreground, a European man in a blue coat and spread-ing white hat, seated on a lattice chair and holding a gun with a long barrel. A big-bottomed black man holds an umbrella over him and keeps flies away with a sprig of leaves. From the right of the picture, a black boy is bringing a big bowl of red liquid on a tray. Lined up at the front are demijohns marked Royal Punch 5 gal., Sangaree 5 gal., brandy. Empty black bottles litter the ground under the planter's seat.

To the left, a third black man switches flies off a table spread with food: a fish, a sucking-pig and a leg of meat. In the distant middle ground, a second planter is lying on a striped camelback sofa under an umbrella held by a mulatto woman. Further back still, a black boy is running with wide outstretched arms, while birds rise all about him in squiggly Vs. At the base of the print is the caption: 'Make haste with the Sangaree, Quashie, and tell Quaco to drive the birds up to me – I'm ready' and the date: Pub. Nov. 1, 1807. I turn back towards Katherine's room, past the open french window where the light makes my eyes ache. Peters, in a brown singlet and shorts, is carrying a bucket of something for his tethered goat. The gardener is on his knees clipping the sweet-lime hedge by the chapel. I turn round and Anne is behind me, in her new nightgown. She takes Katherine without waking her. I walk five steps to our room and lie on the side of the bed which Anne has made warm.

We breakfasted late. I said: 'Maybe we should get the US papers.'

'Relax. You're unemployed now.'

'We could go to the beach. Katherine might love it.'

Peters put down a plate of cut pineapple. 'Not this side,' he said. 'Saint James.'

Peters drove with excruciating slowness. We got behind a tractor pulling a trailer heaped with cut cane. Canes littered the road and crunched under our wheels. Peters swung out on a corner and overtook. The road curved and burrowed into the canes. We came to a crossroads, with an old-fashioned four-way signpost and a woman standing in the shade of a black umbrella. She had on white stockings, a blue satin dress and a red hat with a veil. She carried a fan.

Peters stopped and let her in at the front. Her hat brushed the car hood. She was wearing a sweet scent. She chattered with Peters in an accent I couldn't follow.

'Relax,' said Anne.

The road ended in a half-built roundabout. We passed an earth satellite station and a water-bottling factory. Peters shuddered his way up a ridge past raw new houses, each with a sprig of bougainvillea flowering out of the churned-up clay. Katherine tried to clamber onto the back shelf and, turning to pull her down, I saw a line of Japanese cars behind us.

'Quite soon there'll be no island left,' I said. Nobody said anything.

We crept round another roundabout and came into a district of narrower streets lined with gabled wooden houses painted pink, green or brown. Men squatted on the steps of Banks beer-stands. We crossed a main road, zigzagged down a hill and burst out in front of a big hotel. Across the entrance was a striped metal bar, as at a frontier. A young Barbadian in an unbuttoned uniform leaned back on a metal chair against the guard-house.

'Only tourists allowed,' said Peters. The woman giggled. He said: 'I'll come back at noon, after church.'

He put our things carefully on the sidewalk and drove off.

'That does it,' said Anne. 'We're not moving here.'

Past the guard was a dusty lane which ran down between wind-blown casuarina trees to a hole of sea and sky. As we approached, a football flew past, going over and over, then three white boys in long shorts scrambling up high to catch it. The trees opened on a white beach and a sea green as soap, windsurfers, waterbikers, a girl being pulled through the air underneath a parachute, women lying face down on white slatted beachbeds. Anne let our her breath, as if she were expelling anger. Her shoulders sagged.

I said: 'Let's try up the beach.'

We trudged past a restaurant with thatched tables and found a space in the shade of a beached catamaran.

I spread Katherine's things on a towel. I said: 'I'm going to look for a 'phone.'

'Richard, this thing is getting seriously out of hand.'

'I'll take her. You swim.'

The hotel had a dial 'phone on the sticky bar. A tanned woman in a strapless bikini-top looked at me, then at Katherine, and looked away. I bought an old *Wall Street Journal* in the hotel shop, then came out by some dustbins into a wood of palms. Black birds with yellow eyes strutted about. A grey-haired woman swept the sand with a banana-leaf. A pair of Rastafarians lounged with machetes by a coconut cart.

'Nice kid, daddy!'

A man and a girl leaned on a telephone box. As I came up, they slid away and came together like water on the other side, where they stayed. The 'phone was touch-tone. I put Katherine down among some coconut shells, which she reached out for and put in her mouth.

0–617–472–0375.

Silence flooded the receiver. Then a woman's recorded voice saying: 'Please key in your credit card number now.'

672–180–6305–7146.

'Thank you for using AT & T.'

I imagined my call racing up through the United States, past Miami, Atlanta, Richmond, New York; come flying into Boston in a snowstorm; swerve round the steps of Faneuil Hall and into State Street; and there, with one more flourish, enter the high portals of Provident Securities.

'Welcome to Provident Securities. Please key in your Provident account number now.'

*2*40907642929*4365#
'Thank you.'

I heard faint, satisfactory sounds, like tumblers falling into place in a safe lock. I looked down and Katherine was pulling experimentally at my sneaker laces.

'For stock quotes, press 1. For mutual fund information, press 2. For account information, press 3. To place a trade, press 4. For all other Provident services, press 9 and wait for a . . .'

3.

A new voice spoke, dissonant, slow, like the voice of a deaf woman who has learned speech: an electronic voice spliced out of hundreds of recorded sounds: 'As of november two your provident preferred customer account balance stood at three hundred and sixty-seven thousand and nine hundred and seventy-six dollars and twenty-four cents your provident preferred customer insured money-market account balance was three hundred and sixty-seven thousand and nine hundred and seventy-six dollars and twenty-four cents so far this month you have earned one hundred dollars and eighty-one cents your last money-market dividend was . . .'

I picked up Katherine and walked back through the trees. Three hundred and sixty-eight thousand dollars walked back to the beach. Anne was standing in the water, her swimming costume wet only to the waist. Her arms were laid on the water. She turned round and smiled and then her face went blank with alarm.

'Where's Katherine?'

Green sea, blue sky, parachute, boat, white beach, woman trailing towel, coconut palms, telephone, picnic group, coconut sellers, banana-leaf sweeper, catamaran, striped towel.

'She's under the catamaran,' I said. 'I thought she'd be better in the shade. It's almost noon.'

We didn't go to that side of the island again. Anne broke the day into pieces, then placed them round the garden at Mullins as in a child's treasure hunt: breakfast on the balcony, a swim in the pool before the sun was too high, a rest for Katherine, up to the canes at sundown to see if the monkeys would come back, bathtime, bedtime, drinktime on the balcony, the swing-seat in the warm darkness after dinner.

My world was contracting and Katherine was growing to fill it. At dinner, facing Anne down yards of Barbadian Hepplewhite, I'd be talking – maybe about living in Agua Fria, which was my new plan – and Anne would nod or say 'mm' and I'd know she wasn't listening but thinking of Katherine: maybe the smell of her hair, how red and gold it was like a Victorian wedding ring, the tight grip of her fingers, the way suddenly her head dropped and she was asleep. We weren't used to servants. We'd hear the cook's voice, Peters speak sharply, a creak of board, the ring of a glass; and we'd say nothing while he served, and the silence filled the dining room and went out through the doors till it met the rattling palms by the chapel and the thump of waves on the windward beach.

'We could take a picnic,' I said after Peters had gone.

'Richard, he said it's dangerous this side.'

'Nobody's going to swim.'

Peters drove us. We passed a ruined windmill and a stone church with a fanlight over the door and leaning gravestones and came out above a long white beach, empty of people for miles on each side till it disappeared in mist and spray. He left us by a house with collapsed timber and buckled iron roof. A spiny plant snaked across the surface of the sand.

I laid out the picnic on the towel: grilled flying-fish for us, peas-and-rice in an orange plastic bowl, strained christophine for Katherine. She lay on her back, naked but for her sunbonnet. She took up my sunglasses; looked at them; dropped them on the towel; picked up the Banks bottle-top; put it in her mouth; dropped it by the sunglasses; picked up the sunglasses in one hand and the bottle-top in the other; dropped the bottle-top; looked at me; laughed; dropped the sunglasses. A car grew large on the road, became a sound, sped past, dark with people waving and crying and fluttering a tee-shirt, diminished.

'Nobody's fucking going to swim.'

I got up and walked down to the water's edge. The sand was soft like powder. I walked where the sea had wet the sand and the going was easier. There were no shorebirds to be seen. I looked round and Anne had her back to me, bent over Katherine, perhaps putting some sunscreen on her. There was sand on the bottom of Anne's pink swimsuit. The sun warmed my neck. Water ran over my insteps and sucked the sand pleasantly from between my toes. I thought: after the movers had finished at Grand Street, and the apartment was just as I'd first seen it, with its bare brick walls and scuffed elm boards, snow in the skylight, the roar of an extractor fan from the restaurant below, I thought: what was there here that I needed so much for two years and four months? The Currier and Ives prints? The Gardner service I packed myself? Fire irons wrapped in plastic sheet? A cigar of newspaper that was probably Anne's flute? A plastic baby's bath that Katherine doesn't use any more but, still, worth keeping – a sister takes shape and vanishes – in a way?

The sun was hot on my neck. Cool water splashed my shins. I felt the outgoing wave dig out a hole beneath each foot. I looked up and I was six feet from the dry sand, then double that. The water was at my knees. I stepped smartly back towards the beach but the wave took my feet from under me. Anne and Katherine swept away. I could see the striped towel, the orange bowl, the bottle of Banks, the spine of Anne's paperback. I went down on my hands but the rip tide upended me. Sand swirled in the turbid water. My mouth filled with water and sand.

I thought: I am drowning in thigh-deep water. *Invito Ricardo Verey. Amante nihilominus munditias.* I am gabbling epitaph Latin. *Aquâ nimium inundante.* Calm! Jump forward on the incoming wave, hold the ground on the outgoing (but the suck of sand digs out a hole and the forward wave buries my feet again). I overbalance and slide out, the sand grazing my chest. Anne is standing, holding Katherine by both hands, as if trying to make her take a step. In her sunbonnet, she looks like the watercolour Billy did of me at Studland. 'Anne.' My mouth is full of salt and sand. I need to cry for help but how can you help. 'Anne,' I whisper.

My legs ache. My legs tremble. Calm! You'll die if you go on fighting the tide. Stand still and let it take us down, down the beach. Maybe there's a rock, the remains of a boat, something to hang onto, a place where a stream comes in. Anne is a red figure, shielding her eyes. She bends down and straightens, but her posture is different: bent at the hip, weight on one leg. She must have picked Katherine up. She moves down towards the water.

The wave takes my feet out, spins me round. My ears roar in the green water. My face bumps on the bottom. My trunks are full of sand. I am sliding down but then a big wave comes back over me, pushing me up towards the shore, pushing my legs back under me so I land on my knees. It is shallower, just up to my chest when I'm kneeling and though I slip back down, the big wave again comes and pushes me in and I twist and land on my feet and run a step. Hold! Hold! The sand runs out from under my feet but, here it comes, the incoming wave and I am running up. I feel cold wind on my shins, firm sand underfoot, dry sand.

I lie down with my face inland.

When I got back to Anne, she said: 'Maybe we should go to England. I'll find something. Maybe you should touch base.'

'Maybe.'

While Katherine was going to bed, I walked out to the chapel. The door was on the latch. It scratched on the stone threshold. Inside, the garden floodlights made big shadows of fluttering leaves. I sat in the last of six dark pews. I remembered something I'd read, probably in Latin again, about a fisherman who survived shipwreck and hung his dripping clothes in the temple of Neptune. I knelt down on the stone floor, put my face in my hands as I had done as a child, looked up again. I got up off my knees and sat down.

'What are you thinking about?' I hadn't heard Anne

come in. She sat down beside me and laid her head on my shoulder. She was carrying Katherine's empty bottle.

'Money. What else?'

'Get rid of it, why not? Why not spend some time with us?' She lifted her head and kissed me on the cheek.

I stood up. Through the window, across the garden into the dining room, I could see Peters, in his clean white shirt, filling our glasses from a water jug.

The next day, I gave Katherine her breakfast, while Anne lay in. As usual, a sparrow perched on Katherine's tray. She reached out helplessly for it, laughing. I made toast soldiers and dipped them into an egg for her, but she didn't want them so I ate them myself. I put her down in the shade of the frangipani while I read *Business Week*, but she got stuck on her front and began to scream. I picked her up and took her to the swing-seat. The gardener was cutting the lawn with edge-clippers. He raised his hand in a shy salute.

I wiped the dew off the seat with my arm and sat down. I took Katherine on my lap, and crossed my arms round her chest. We began to swing gently. She chuckled. I could feel the laughter start in her small chest and climb up, under my crossed arm.

I looked at the chapel before me. It was beautiful: ochre walls, red tiles, green trees, green lawn, blue sky. Not only the colour but the composition was beautiful: from the left a gothic buttress, a lead gutter, a niche with a green statuette of a saint, two gothic windows (a little askew) and then four royal palms their grey trunks soaring high above the roof, then another buttress on the right. Katherine wriggled and I closed my arms tight around her.

I was thinking about what Anne had said. Perhaps I should get rid of the money at Provident, give it away or gamble it away. My mother never had money. My father never had money. Billy Baird never had a penny. But I was posted to Kuwait, and saved £10,000 in 1979 money, which luck and inflation have multiplied twenty times.

For eight years, I've dragged this money round with me. I've counted it in dinars, pounds, Deutsche Mark, dollars. I've moved it from a savings account at the National Bank of Kuwait into stock in Daimler Benz, a mortgaged house in Gospel Oak, United States Treasury Bills, a few put options on the Standard & Poor's 500 Index – which, on 19 October, when everything else seemed worthless, swelled atrociously in value – , finally a money market account at Provident Securities in Boston.

This money is ruining me, twisting my nature, spoiling my marriage. I have to watch it in case it loses value. At each move, it sheds chips off the side to bankers, stockbrokers, real estate agents, the Inland Revenue, the IRS. It unnerves me. I can't work, because it works for me, all day, while I sleep, earning more than I can earn. I must give it away: maybe to that centre on 42nd Street that Anne likes – they won't know what hit them, $370,000 in the mail – or maybe something here, a clinic, the Katherine Verey Clinic, or something to do with conservation. Or maybe I should just put it back where I found it, in the financial markets. I could buy something really awful, the junkiest of junk securities, something yielding 30 or 40 per cent, bankruptcy bait, and if it doesn't go bust, well, I'll put it in something else that will.

Katherine cried out and tried to wriggle free. She was bored with the swing and the view of the chapel. I put a foot down, to stop the swing, and she slipped right through my arms and through my legs; and, as she slid down, she chuckled again at this new thing; and, as I jumped forward – chapel, palm trees, lawn – I saw her face again, the delight going out and the surprise coming in, and the big swing-seat behind her, askew, and then that was all I saw because the seat hit me in the face and I filled up with rage and light.

The seat hit me again, but then I caught it, set it to rest. There was something important happening, but I couldn't quite say what it was. Ahead of me, across the low sweet-lime hedge, the gardener is peering at me, his brown eyes full of surprise. I look round to my left and Peters is running, in a brown singlet and dark shorts, arms pumping up and down like an athlete, while a steel bucket turns over and over in the air, spilling mango skins and potato peelings. To my right, Anne is also running, in her bathing suit and new dressing gown, her new sunglasses slipping off her nose, one shoe in the air and the other just detaching from her foot.

I turn round and see Katherine. She is lying with her cheek on the grass, as I've never seen her before. The half of her face I can see is quite pale, as I've never seen it before. I can see no mark from the swing-seat but her bonnet has slipped to the back of her head. I pick her up, cupping her warm head in my right hand, but Anne pushes past me and I give her up. The look on Anne's face is like – if this is possible – a door closing. It is quiet. There is not a sound: no birds, no monkeys, no sea, not even a breadfruit falling in the swimming-pool.

And then it comes, the sound I'm listening for but it still surprises me, the sound of God's unfathomable mercy, which is also the sound of a small child screaming.

TEN

Coming Home

When we came back from the United States, we lived for a time in Dorset, near where I'd been at school. We rented a place outside Wareham while we looked for something to buy. Anne worked in the mornings and one afternoon a week at a family practice in Poole, while I looked after Katherine. When my writing wasn't going well, I picked quarrels with Anne, though I knew it wasn't her fault or Katherine's.

Weekends were difficult. We hadn't met anybody we liked. We went to the sea at Studland, where I'd been as a child, but Katherine ate sand. We saw Wareham church, Bovington camp and T. E. Lawrence's cottage. At Hardy's house in Dorchester, I bought a National Trust guide. The nearest house to Wareham open to the public was called The Vale.

' "Interesting ornamental and exotic trees." '

Anne was washing up lunch. I'd cooked.

' "Pictures attributed to Kneller, Wouvermans, Batoni." '

Anne put a teapot upside down on the draining board.

' "Objects of naval interest. In the stables, a collection of early racing automobiles.

' "From Wareham, a pleasant walk on signed paths. 3 mi." I bet I went there with my Pa from school.'

(My father drove down from London once a term. He never came to the front door and never asked me to bring a friend. After chapel, I changed my shoes and walked to the first cattle grid, where he was sitting in a grey Ford Cortina, smoking a Rothmans in a holder and drinking coffee from a thermos. We had lunch in the King's Head in Wareham: roast beef, with red wine to drink and coffee. After lunch, whether it was raining or sunny, we drove off to see a country house. Of these places, I can remember only a mausoleum and a tower, and worn steps that wound up to a golden ball on an iron spire and, below, a view down on trees. Perhaps this first sight of tree-tops rescued the memory for me or perhaps it was the new word mausoleum. On the drive back to school, my father talked about the families that had built and vacated these big houses, how they intersected our family and how he had last seen old so-and-so at the Ritz in Paris before the war, where he sat on his hand and broke it. I once repeated some of this at school, and was teased all one wet Saturday afternoon and then, for the next year or two, whenever I was teased, I was teased also about this.)

Anne had turned round from the sink. She said: 'You don't have to be like your father, you know.'

I took Katherine in a back-pack I'd bought on Avenue A, but she was too big for it, kept standing up and driving the frame into the small of my back. Anne walked ahead of us, a jumper tied round her waist and, stuffed into it, a pink Ordnance Survey map.

The footpath went up through a field of sunflowers to an open down. The path was worn a foot deep into the chalk. We kept coming to roads with just too much traffic. At each road crossing, there was a fancy hand-lettered sign to The Vale.

I could see from Anne's back that she found these excruciatingly provoking. I tried to look at the country through her eyes. I saw small hills almost swamped with big fields, green corn lapping at the top of the down, couples with dogs, hang-gliders. What does she bloody expect? I shut my eyes and tried to call back America: a stone house we saw on a walk from the farm, all tumbled into its cellar-hole and apple-trees run wild and plastered with gun-club notices, or an abandoned holiday camp, further up towards Slide, with a Star of David just visible on the flaking dormitory huts.

At a stile, I unhitched Katherine to rest my sore kidneys. She was asleep with her sunbonnet askew. Anne stood with her hands on her hips, squinting into the glare.

After an hour, we came down into a valley full of old beeches, passed an iron fence and a pair of gate posts and saw The Vale at the other end of a gravel drive. The house had a portico of plain columns of yellowish stone and two colonnaded wings in front, like a miniature St. Peter's. In the left-hand colonnade, there was a machine which sold tickets to the house for £5 each. A guidebook, its pages sheathed in polythene, hung on a hook. There was nobody about. The heat off the gravel was terrific.

The house was cool. We walked through on a neat cord runner roped off from the main part of the rooms. Anne went on ahead while I worked through the guide. The pictures were mostly large portraits of men in eighteenth-century costume, with wigs on their heads and swords at their sides, and beyond them, through a window or under a furled curtain, ships arrayed at sea. I saw the camp bed which Nelson had slept in before Copenhagen. On small tables and sideboards, there were family photographs in new silver or leather frames. They were everywhere. Anne was two rooms ahead, so I looked at the photographs.

They were all of a woman with thick and beautiful black hair, and two small children. They sat, curled up on a fur rug before a blazing fire, the children in black knickerbockers or on a stone seat outside, in busy ruffs of lace, with the sun making haloes of their hair. In some of the photographs, there was also a man. He had his hand gently on the lady's shoulder or teetered just outside the group, as if he had posed his family with a time switch and strode round to insert himself. He was fat, with short hair inexpertly cut.

Anne was standing by an open french window, where another hand-lettered sign pointed to Garden and Arboretum.

'Big deal,' she said.

I said: 'Might as well see these famous ornamental trees.'

We came out onto a hot terrace bounded by a balustrade. Beyond the balustrade was a lawn and then a wilderness of trees and rhododendrons. In the middle was a big copper beech. It looked a good shady walk for Katherine, but the way down from the terrace was by a flight of stone steps and between us and the steps was a table with people sitting among coffee-cups and wine-bottles. The man and the woman from the photograph were there and two others, a couple; no children. Anne stopped. I started forward and stopped. I didn't think I could pass so close to the table without saying something.

Anne clicked her tongue against her teeth.

I said: 'Did you see Admiral Nelson's camp bed?'

We walked back through the rooms. In the last, the dark-haired woman was struggling with a catch at the top of a french door. She had on a white skirt and jacket of some shiny silk: better for a wedding than a small lunch party. She was standing on tip-toe. The skirt seam had split at the hip.

She said: 'Are you being looked after? What a sweet baby.'

She smiled without welcome. I regretted my walking boots, the jumper round Anne's waist, the back-pack.

I said: 'Thank you. Very nice house.'

She had both sides of the french door open. She took a step into the room, hesitated, then walked quickly to the rope and started trying to unhook it. She said quickly: 'Peter's going to do his tour of the garden. We have some people with us. Would you like to come?'

She'd got the rope free and was holding it up. Anne looked at me.

'Thank you very much,' I said.

Anne paused to let me through first.

Outside at the table, the men were standing. Peter was wearing shorts, white socks to the knee and black shoes. He was smiling. The other man was much taller and slimmer. He wore a pink shirt, pressed blue jeans and a Gucci belt and Gucci shoes. His hand lay lightly but expressively on the back of a chair where a girl sat, her face hidden by a wide-brimmed hat. She turned and smiled faintly at Katherine. They looked like spongers.

Peter moved heavily towards me. I thought of introducing myself and Anne and put my hand half out to shake, but he said: 'Welcome. Welcome.'

I put it out again, but he was off down the steps, sideways. We followed him to the middle of the lawn, where he stopped, his legs a little apart.

He was saying: 'These are Norfolk Island Pines which the first Admiral Terry planted. That was in 1781. He thought they might supply the Navy at Portsmouth with timber for ships' masts. You see how straight they grow. Anyway, they didn't really thrive. This here is the celebrated Cannonball Tree, also brought back by the first Admiral, from the West Indies.'

We wound into the rhododendrons on dusty paths. Katherine chattered on my back. The spongers pointed things out to each other in soft voices, like newly weds. Anne fussed with Katherine's sunbonnet. I swung at the hips, to show the back-pack was heavy. The dark-haired woman, who had stopped at the table while a Portuguese or Spanish maid in a blue uniform came out with a tray, caught us up. She was out of breath. She found it difficult to walk in high-heeled shoes. She smiled at Katherine.

'We have twins,' she said. 'Asleep now.'

I said: 'I suppose you've lived down here for ever.'

'Oh no! Peter always liked it down here, when he

was young, so when the poor family had to, you know; we, you know. We live in town most of the week. We open the house and garden for the grants, you know.'

'We very much admired the signs on the way.'

'Oh, I must tell Peter. He did them all himself.'

Peter was standing by the copper beech and was looking shyly at us. We hurried up, turned in the direction he was facing and saw the house in full, the steps to the terrace, the balustrade, the maid clearing the table. Peter said: 'It appears that the Admiral never saw this elevation completed. There's a letter from St. Lucia, dated Dec. 6, 1802, where he changed the specification from brick to Purbeck stone. On the whole, we're rather glad.'

His wife whispered to Anne: 'Do you live nearby?'

'Wareham.'

I strode forward with Katherine, who woke up, mewed like a seagull, and fell asleep again. I stood apart, as if she needed quiet to sleep. I rolled my shoulders. I wanted to say: Ma'am, you won't get much help from Anne, I can tell you, but don't worry. England is a small country and the class thing makes it smaller. If we haven't met, you've met people we've met somewhere, some time. You need one or two more conversational bracketing shots. Imagine you're playing Battleships.

Look: Anne and I don't care if you've owned this place a week. We don't care that your husband is what the English call a bore. He's thick-skinned, rich, intelligent, quite gentle probably. Don't worry about the spongers: they don't think much of us either; I can hear them saying, wherever they're going next: he had their child in a kind of knapsack thing, can you imagine?

England isn't that bad once you get used to it. You'd be a lot worse off in Bucharest or wherever you come from.

I was back below the terrace. Peter was on the top step, standing side-on, smiling. His posture was heroic, military. I wondered if he had one of the portraits in mind. In his shorts and knee-socks, he looked like a schoolboy who had suddenly doubled in size. The spongers stepped past him and walked towards the house, as if to go to their rooms: to bathe, I thought, or telephone but not to make love. Peter dropped his pose and turned to face me. He said: 'Have you seen the racing cars? You've done the mausoleum?'

'I think,' I said, 'that maybe we should be beginning to think of. . . .'

The two women came up. Anne looked flustered. The dark-haired woman said between breaths: 'Pee, our visitors know Johnny and Katie Morrison. They've taken one of the farm cottages at Hinton Parva. What an amazing coincidence!'

Peter looked puzzled.

I put my hand out: 'I'm Richard Verey. And this is my wife, Anne Keenan.'

Peter looked down at my hand and up at my face. He looked crestfallen. He said: 'Scrimper Verey?'

'No. That's my cousin. He was in your year.'

'Ah,' said Peter. 'Your hair's much darker now than it was then.'

I said: 'Your father had a Rolls-Royce.'

Peter smiled and looked down. 'So, alas, have I. This is my wife, Yvona.'

'With a Y at the beginning,' she said. We shook hands.

Yvona said: 'Pee, perhaps Mr and Mrs Verey would like to have a glass of wine.'

The spongers were at the french door. They looked back and walked in. Anne looked at me.

I said: 'This little one. Home. Walking. Time. Tired. Tea.' I swung at the waist and Katherine stirred.

'Of course,' Yvona said quickly. 'Of course. Poor little thing. We have twin boys. You must.'

'Maybe, Richard, we could . . .'

'You must visit us if you come to Wareham.' I felt in my back pocket and came up with the business card of the plumber who fixed the washing-machine. I wrote our address and telephone number on it. I offered it to Peter, but he was looking at me closely, as if he were searching my face for a likeness to a schoolboy he knew.

'Are you in business, too?' I said. 'I mean like your father.'

His gaze relaxed. 'Sort of. Next time, you must see the Admiral's mausoleum.'

Anne and I didn't say anything until we reached the gates to the road. Then Anne turned round to face me, and walking backwards, said: 'I'd've stayed, Richard. We could've given her her tea there. They'd've had something for her, sure. They've got twins. Jesus, what's the point of all this circling about, this ass-sniffing, round and round to establish if we're suitable to know and they're suitable to know, if you're just going to reject the possibility of intimacy. I hate this fucking country so much. I hate the way you change on me when you're with people like that. I hate the way you're

133

all such fucking snobs. You're stunted, you're deformed by snobbery. If I were you, I'd get out of here, go back to the United States, or at least to Edith's or somewhere, somewhere where nobody knows us or has any idea about us or cares who we are, where we can be a family again . . .'

Katherine stirred on my back. She began to complain. Anne turned round and quickened her step, tying her jumper as she went. In one minute, or five minutes, or ten minutes, Katherine was going to be screaming with hunger and tiredness.

It was windy on the top. Anne again turned round and, still walking backwards, threw out her arms in greeting. She cried: 'Stinker, old fellow! My dear Tom-Tit!'

But something had softened in her. She waited for us to catch up and took Katherine's hand and since that calmed the child, walked with us, holding her hand. The path turned downhill. I began to run and Katherine sang out because she liked the wind in her face.

What I was thinking was this, but I didn't say it to Anne, because she is a woman who is not interested in statements that can't be remotely verified. I thought: I don't mind this English thing, it's not that, it's not that. It's just that I never thought until now we would end up just like our parents; that Peter Smith, with his Rolls-Royce and dubious business, is indistinguishable from his father; and that I still trail round other people's houses, not envious but well-informed, like my own father; and that all these years and all these places and all the feeling we had, when I was with Julie, that we, we would be different, have not meant a great deal;

and that these episodes in my life, which I have written down with all the precision I can manage, leaving out everything that can be left out, are not very important except as exercises in recollection; and that if my mother hadn't died, and Felicia not gone off or Kurt Axel been murdered, things might not have been very much different. I might not be here, in this ridiculous landscape, hurrying down with my wife and child towards the tower of Wareham church, but I would still be I, Richard Verey, thirty-five years old, an Englishman of the upper middle class.

A Selected List of Fiction Available from Minerva

While every effort is made to keep prices low, it is sometimes necessary to increase prices at short notice. Mandarin Paperbacks reserves the right to show new retail prices on covers which may differ from those previously advertised in the text or elsewhere.

The prices shown below were correct at the time of going to press.

☐	7493 9145 6	**Love and Death on Long Island**	Gilbert Adair	£4.99
☐	7493 9130 8	**The War of Don Emmanuel's Nether Parts**	Louis de Bernieres	£5.99
☐	7493 9903 1	**Dirty Faxes**	Andrew Davies	£4.99
☐	7493 9056 5	**Nothing Natural**	Jenny Diski	£4.99
☐	7493 9173 1	**The Trick is to Keep Breathing**	Janice Galloway	£4.99
☐	7493 9124 3	**Honour Thy Father**	Lesley Glaister	£4.99
☐	7493 9918 X	**Richard's Feet**	Carey Harrison	£6.99
☐	7493 9028 X	**Not Not While the Giro**	James Kelman	£4.99
☐	7493 9112 X	**Hopeful Monsters**	Nicholas Mosley	£6.99
☐	7493 9029 8	**Head to Toe**	Joe Orton	£4.99
☐	7493 9117 0	**The Good Republic**	William Palmer	£5.99
☐	7493 9162 6	**Four Bare Legs in a Bed**	Helen Simpson	£4.99
☐	7493 9134 0	**Rebuilding Coventry**	Sue Townsend	£4.99
☐	7493 9151 0	**Boating for Beginners**	Jeanette Winterson	£4.99
☐	7493 9915 5	**Cyrus Cyrus**	Adam Zameenzad	£7.99

All these books are available at your bookshop or newsagent, or can be ordered direct from the publisher. Just tick the titles you want and fill in the form below.

Mandarin Paperbacks, Cash Sales Department, PO Box 11, Falmouth, Cornwall TR10 9EN.

Please send cheque or postal order, no currency, for purchase price quoted and allow the following for postage and packing:

UK including BFPO — £1.00 for the first book, 50p for the second and 30p for each additional book ordered to a maximum charge of £3.00.

Overseas including Eire — £2 for the first book, £1.00 for the second and 50p for each additional book thereafter.

NAME (Block letters) ....

ADDRESS ....

....

☐ I enclose my remittance for ....

☐ I wish to pay by Access/Visa Card Number ☐☐☐☐☐☐☐☐☐☐☐☐☐☐☐☐

Expiry Date ☐☐☐☐